PENGUIN CLASSICS

A Complete Annotated Listing of
Penguin Classics and Twentieth-Century Classics

TABLE OF CONTENTS

A NOTE TO THE READER

For fifty years, Penguin has been the leading publisher of the classics of world literature in the English-speaking world. Since the publication of the first Penguin Classic in 1946—E. V. Rieu's translation of *The Odyssey*—we have dedicated ourselves to making sure that the great books of all time speak to the present day by reflecting the state of the art in scholarship, translation, and book design. We also continue to honor our founder Allen Lane's original mission: to make these great books available at a reasonable cost.

This new catalog provides complete, annotated descriptions of all books currently available in our Classics and Twentieth-Century Classics series. We've also noted when new audiocassette versions of these great titles are available from our Penguin·HighBridge or Penguin Classics on Audio lines.

From Renaissance philosophy to the poetry of revolutionary Russia, from the spiritual writings of India to the travel narratives of the early American colonists, from the Age of Homer to the Beat epic *On the Road,* there are Classics here to educate, provoke, entertain, and enlighten readers of all interests and inclinations. We hope this catalog will inspire you to pick up that book you've always been meaning to read, or the one you may not have heard of before.

We'd love to hear your thoughts about the Penguin Classics, and to include your name on our mailing list to receive our *Classics Chronicle* newsletter and other information. Please write to us at Penguin Classics, Dept. MEC, 375 Hudson Street, New York, NY 10014.

Classics titles available on audiocassette from
Penguin·HighBridge or Penguin Audiobooks are indicated with the symbol

ART AND ARCHITECTURE

HENRY ADAMS
1839–1918, AMERICAN

Mont Saint Michel and Chartres

Introduced by Raymond Carney

A philosophical and historical meditation on the human condition, Adams's journey into the medieval consciousness synthesizes literature, art, politics, science, and psychology.

398 pp.   0-14-039054-5 $ 9.95

LEON BATTISTA ALBERTI
1404–1472, ITALIAN

On Painting

Edited and introduced by Martin Kemp
Translated by Cecil Grayson

The first book devoted to the intellectual rationale for painting, Alberti's discussion of the process of vision, painting techniques, and the moral and artistic prerequisites of the artist remains a classic of art theory.

112 pp.   0-14-043331-7 $ 8.95

BENVENUTO CELLINI
1500–1571, ITALIAN

Autobiography

Translated by George Bull

With enviable powers of invective and an irrepressible sense of humor, Cellini provides an unrivaled portrait of the manners and morals of the Renaissance Italy of Michelangelo and the Medici.

400 pp.   0-14-044049-6 $ 8.95

GEORG WILHELM FRIEDRICH HEGEL
1770–1831, GERMAN

Introductory Lectures on Aesthetics

Introduced with a commentary by Michael Inwood
Translated by Bernard Bosanquet

Hegel's writings on art—and his profound conclusion that art was in terminal decline—demonstrate the broad impact of his thinking on our culture.

240 pp.   0-14-043335-X $ 10.95

WILLIAM MORRIS
1834–1896, ENGLISH

News from Nowhere and Other Writings

For a description, see LITERATURE.

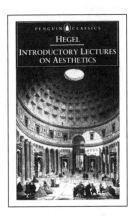

SIR JOSHUA REYNOLDS
1723–1792, ENGLISH

Discourses

Edited and introduced by Pat Rogers

The art criticism and philosophical essays of Sir Joshua Reynolds, England's masterful portrait painter and literary stylist, were first presented to the students of the Royal Academy, after he became its first president in 1768.

432 pp.   0-14-043278-7 $ 10.95

GIORGIO VASARI
1511–1574, ITALIAN

Lives of the Artists
Volume 1

Translated, edited, and introduced by George Bull

Vasari offers insights into the lives and techniques of twenty artists from Cimabue, Giotto, and Leonardo to Michelangelo and Titian.

480 pp.   0-14-044500-2 $ 9.95

Lives of the Artists
Volume 2

Translated, edited, and introduced by George Bull

Vasari's firsthand knowledge was based on his own experience as an early Renaissance painter and architect. Volume 2 explores the lives of twenty-five artists, from Perugino to Giovanni Pisano.

376 pp.   0-14-044460-5 $ 9.95

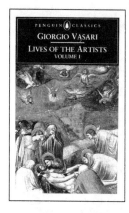

AUTOBIOGRAPHY AND BIOGRAPHY

The Pillow Book of Sei Shōnagon

Translated by Ivan Morris

This detailed account of the daily life of a court lady in tenth-century Japan at the height of the Heian culture is a work of lively humor and great literary beauty.

416 pp.   0-14-044236-7 $ 8.95

ABÉLARD and HÉLOÏSE
1079–C.1144, 1101–1164, FRENCH

The Letters of Abélard and Héloïse

Translated and introduced by Betty Radice

This collection of writings offers insight into the minds of two prominent medieval figures—the French Scholastic philosopher Peter Abélard and his beloved Héloïse, who became a learned abbess.

312 pp.   0-14-044297-9 $ 8.95

HENRY ADAMS
1838–1918, AMERICAN

The Education of Henry Adams

For a description, see HISTORY AND POLITICS.

JOHN AUBREY
1626–1697, ENGLISH

Aubrey's Brief Lives

Edited and introduced by Oliver Lawson Dick

Sometimes ribald, but always observant, these writings capture the personalities of some of the most intriguing figures of the seventeenth century.

400 pp.   0-14-043079-2 $ 8.95

AUGUSTINE
354–430, CHRISTIAN SAINT

Confessions

For a description, see RELIGION.

JAMES BOSWELL
1740–1795, SCOTTISH

The Life of Samuel Johnson

Edited by Christopher Hibbert

This classic biography, completed in 1791, is based on Boswell's conversations with Johnson, documents and letters, and anecdotes from friends, all shaped by Boswell's incomparable wit and originality. Abridged.

384 pp.   0-14-043116-0 $ 9.95

VERA BRITTAIN
1896–1970, ENGLISH

Testament of Youth

Vera Brittain's pacifist and feminist memoir of the First World War, in which she served as a nurse in London, Malta, and in France at the front, is a classic account of an entire generation marked by fatal idealism and changed by war.

20TH-CENTURY CLASSICS

672 pp.   0-14-018844-4 $ 14.95

JOHN BUNYAN
1628–1688, ENGLISH

Grace Abounding to the Chief of Sinners

For a description, see RELIGION.

OLAUDAH EQUIANO
1745–1797, NIGERIAN

The Interesting Narrative and Other Writings

For a description, see LITERATURE.

BENJAMIN FRANKLIN
1706–1790, AMERICAN

The Autobiography and Other Writings

Introduced by Kenneth A. Silverman

Franklin's best known work of literature traces his rise from a printer's apprentice to an internationally famous scientist, inventor, statesman, legislator, and diplomat.

320 pp.   0-14-039052-9 $ 5.95

ELIZABETH GASKELL
1810–1865, ENGLISH

The Life of Charlotte Brontë

Edited by Alan Shelston

Novelist Elizabeth Gaskell drew on her friendship with the author of *Jane Eyre*, *Shirley*, and *Villette* to write this psychologically compelling portrait of Brontë, whose controversial works belied the reclusive life she led.

624 pp.   0-14-043099-7 $ 9.95

HAMLIN GARLAND
1860–1940, AMERICAN

A Son of the Middle Border

Introduced by Joseph B. McCullough

Mining the history of his own family, Garland's bittersweet narrative about growing up on a Wisconsin farm is an epic of America's immigration toward new frontiers in the nineteenth century and of the gradual disillusionment with the pioneer ideal.

20TH-CENTURY CLASSICS
416 pp.   0-14-018796-0 $ 11.95

EDWARD GIBBON
1737–1794, ENGLISH

Memoirs of My Life

Edited and introduced by Betty Radice

The author of *The Decline and Fall of the Roman Empire* sheds light on some of his more renowned contemporaries and on eighteenth-century life in general in these fascinating memoirs.

224 pp.   0-14-043217-5 $ 10.95

BENJAMIN FRANKLIN
1706–1790, American

Benjamin Franklin, inventor, diplomat, statesman, was also the author of what is considered one of the greatest autobiographies ever written. Begun in 1771, when Franklin was sixty-five years old, it took almost twenty years to complete, its composition interrupted by Franklin's political activities in England and France as well as at home. The *Autobiography* is a truly American story—a success saga that reflects the possibilities open to a smart, ambitious, and eminently practical young man in the New World. From his account of his self-education to his description of how he became a prosperous printer in Philadelphia to a full section devoted to the "Thirteen Virtues" necessary for success, Franklin in many ways created the first "self-improvement" book in American literature.

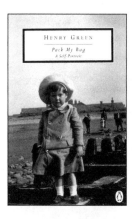

MAXIM GORKY
1868–1936, RUSSIAN

Fragments from My Diary

Translated by Moura Budberg

An idiosyncratic autobiography of Gorky and his country emerges from "fragments" marked by his characteristic storytelling genius.

20TH-CENTURY CLASSICS

288 pp. 0-14-018283-7 $ 8.95

My Apprenticeship

Translated by Ronald Wilks

The second volume of Gorky's autobiographical trilogy records his first encounters with the violent side of Russian life during the later years of the nineteenth century.

20TH-CENTURY CLASSICS

368 pp. 0-14-018284-5 $ 6.95

My Childhood

Translated by Ronald Wilks

The first part of Gorky's autobiographical trilogy, this volume records with charm and poignancy the childhood of extreme poverty and brutality that deepened Gorky's understanding of the "ordinary Russian," an experience that would influence some of his greatest works.

20TH-CENTURY CLASSICS

240 pp. 0-14-018285-3 $ 8.95

My Universities

Translated by Ronald Wilks

In relating his encounters with revolutionaries, religious fanatics, and eccentric scholars, Gorky sheds light on Russian society from 1884 to 1888 and records his growing disenchantment with workers and peasants.

20TH CENTURY CLASSICS

160 pp. 0-14-018286-1 $ 8.95

HENRY GREEN
1905–1973, ENGLISH

Pack My Bag
A Self-Portrait

Introduced by Sebastian Yorke

This mid-life memoir by the incisive Green, full of the same marvelous craft and intuition that he displays in his fiction, was written in 1938, and chronicles his youth, his life at Eton and Oxford, and his first experiments with romance and writing.

20TH-CENTURY CLASSICS

256 pp. 0-14-018793-6 $ 10.95

JAMES WELDON JOHNSON
1871–1938, AMERICAN

Along This Way
The Autobiography of James Weldon Johnson

Introduced by Sondra Kathryn Wilson

A diplomat, politician, pamphleteer, lecturer, and civil rights activist, James Weldon Johnson captured his life and his times in this memoir, an enduring part of twentieth-century American history.

20TH-CENTURY CLASSICS
432 pp.   0-14-018401-5 $ 9.95

MARGERY KEMPE
c. 1373–c. 1440, ENGLISH

The Book of Margery Kempe
Translated and introduced by Barry Windeatt

One of the most engaging of Christian lives, this earliest known English autobiography is a remarkable and touching record of the author's difficult pilgrimage from madness to faith.

336 pp.   0-14-043251-5 $ 10.95

JAMES WELDON JOHNSON
1871–1938, American

James Weldon Johnson, born to a middle-class family in Jacksonville, Florida, in 1871, was a major figure in the creation and development of African-American literature and culture. A twentieth-century Renaissance man, Johnson was the first African-American lawyer admitted to the Florida bar. He was a schoolteacher and principal in his native South before migrating at the turn of the century to New York City, where he enjoyed remarkable success writing musicals for the Broadway stage. Eager to demonstrate the possibilities open to educated blacks, Johnson turned to politics, serving as American consul to Venezuela and Nicaragua. When he returned home, he joined the staff of the NAACP and was appointed its head in 1920; his decade-long tenure saw tremendous growth in both the size and the accomplishments of the organization. As in his public service, as a poet, songwriter, essayist and novelist, Johnson dedicated himself to honoring his roots, championing the artistic achievements of the black community that expressed "the racial spirit by symbols from within rather than by symbols from without." From his pioneering collection of spirituals in *God's Trombones* (see Poetry) to his autobiographical works, to his lyrical poetry of "Saint Peter Relates an Incident," (also in Poetry) Johnson brought to life— and celebrated with humor and dignity—the African-American experience.

PRIMO LEVI
1919–1987, ITALIAN

Moments of Reprieve

Against the terrifying, tragic background of Auschwitz, Levi preserves for future generations the tales of his friends, companions, and even adversaries who shared his hell during the Holocaust.

20TH-CENTURY CLASSICS

176 pp.   0-14-018895-9 $ 10.95

OSIP MANDELSTAM
1891–1938, RUSSIAN

The Noise of Time
The Prose of Osip Mandelstam

For a description, see LITERATURE.

W. SOMERSET MAUGHAM
1874–1965, ENGLISH

The Summing Up

Written to give some account of how Maugham learned his craft and why he became such an acute observer of human beings, reading *The Summing Up* is like having an intimate conversation with one of the great cultured minds of the century.

20TH-CENTURY CLASSICS

208 pp.   0-14-018600-X $ 8.95

A Writer's Notebook

This revealing and curiously intimate collection discloses the sketches and ideas of one of literature's most compelling personalities.

20TH-CENTURY CLASSICS

336 pp.   0-14-018601-8 $ 10.95

JOHN STUART MILL
1806–1873, ENGLISH

Autobiography

*Edited and introduced by
John H. Robson*

This 1873 work by the founder of Britain's Utilitarian Society and the author of *System of Logic* and *Principles of Political Economy* describes Mill's intellectual and moral development from his earliest years to maturity.

240 pp.   0-14-043316-3 $ 8.95

JOHN HENRY NEWMAN
1801–1890, ENGLISH

Apologia pro Vita Sua

For a description, see RELIGION.

FRIEDRICH NIETZSCHE
1844–1900, GERMAN

Ecce Homo

*Introduced by Michael Tanner
Translated by R. J. Hollingdale*

This strange and moving autobiography of Nietzsche, begun in late 1888, weeks before his final psychological breakdown, is one of the masterpieces of German prose.

144 pp.   0-14-044515-3 $ 7.95

DOROTHY OSBORNE
1627–1695, ENGLISH

Letters to Sir William Temple

Edited and introduced by
Kenneth Parker

Expressing ideas and observations
strikingly modern for her day, Dorothy
Osborne's letters (1652–1654) to the
prominent statesman she would later
marry provide a shrewd and thoughtful
commentary on the social and intellectual climate of the Commonwealth
period.

352 pp.   0-14-043265-5 $ 7.95

JEAN RHYS
1894–1979, WEST INDIAN

Letters
1931–1966

Selected and edited by Francis Wyndham
and Diana Melly
Introduced by Francis Wyndham

These letters provide a frank and moving self-portrait of a complex writer
who is regarded as one of the great literary figures of this century. Written by
Rhys while completing *Wide Sargasso
Sea*, it reveals the turbulent process of
literary creation behind her masterpiece.

20TH-CENTURY CLASSICS

320 pp.   0-14-018906-8 $ 10.95

JEAN–JACQUES ROUSSEAU
1712–1778, FRENCH

The Confessions

Translated and introduced by
J. M. Cohen

The posthumously published *Confes-
sions* describes the first fifty-three years
of the author's life, in a masterpiece that
has left an indelible imprint on the
thought of successive generations.

608 pp.   0-14-044033-X $ 7.95

GEORGE SAND
1804–1876, FRENCH

Lettres d'un Voyageur

Introduced by Patricia Thomson
Translated by Sasha Rabinovitch

In these remarkable letters, published as
articles from 1834 to 1836, Sand's controversial approach to life is reflected in
her provocative comments on art, music, religion, politics, and the relations
between the sexes.

368 pp.   0-14-044411-4 $ 9.95

LADY SARASHINA
1008–?, JAPANESE

As I Crossed a Bridge of Dreams
Recollections of a Woman in Eleventh-Century Japan

Translated and introduced by
Ivan Morris

Born at the height of the Heian period,
the pseudonymous Lady Sarashina reveals much about the Japanese literary
tradition in this haunting self-portrait.

176 pp.   0-14-044282-0 $ 7.95

MADAME DE SÉVIGNÉ
1626–1696, FRENCH

Selected Letters
*Edited and translated by
Leonard Tancock*

An extraordinary vivid picture of social, literary, and political life in Louis XIV's France is captured in this selection of letters.

320 pp.   0-14-044405-X $ 10.95

STENDHAL
1788–1842, FRENCH

The Life of Henry Brulard
*Translated and introduced by
John Sturrock*

Frank, sardonic, and wickedly amusing, Stendhal's autobiography reveals a man out of place in his times, not only in his comments on contemporary values, but, most strikingly, in its assumption that childhood experiences shape a man—a belief more compatible to our post-Freudian age than to France in the 1830s. Stendhal's hand-drawn maps and sketches are featured throughout.

560 pp.   0-14-044611-7 $ 12.95

LYTTON STRACHEY
1880–1932, ENGLISH

Eminent Victorians
Introduced by Michael Holroyd

Marking an epoch in the art of biography, this volume has been hailed as "the work of a great anarch, a revolutionary textbook on bourgeois society" (Cyril Connolly).

20TH-CENTURY CLASSICS
272 pp.   0-14-018350-7 $ 9.95

TERESA OF AVILA
1515–1582, SPANISH

The Life of St. Teresa of Avila by Herself
*Translated and introduced by
M. A. Screech*

This story of how a willful and unbalanced woman was transformed by profound religious experiences delves into the nature of exalted states; after *Don Quixote*, it is the most widely read Spanish prose classic.

320 pp.   0-14-044073-9 $ 6.95

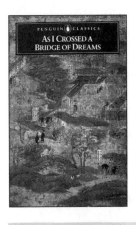

GIORGIO VASARI
1511–1574, ITALIAN

Lives of the Artists
Volume 1

For a description, see ART AND ARCHITECTURE.

Lives of the Artists
Volume 2

For a description, see ART AND ARCHITECTURE.

BOOKER T. WASHINGTON
1856–1915, AMERICAN

Up from Slavery

Introduced by Louis R. Harlan

This autobiography recounts the life of one of the turn of the century's most influential black spokesmen.

336 pp.   0-14-039051-0 $ 7.95

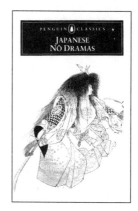

DRAMA

English Mystery Plays
A Selection

Edited by Peter Happé

These thirty-seven mystery plays, written during the late medieval period to celebrate the Christian story from *The Fall of Lucifer* to *Judgment Day*, significantly influenced the work of later dramatists.

720 pp.   0-14-043093-8 $ 10.95

Five Italian Renaissance Comedies

Edited by Bruce Penman

Rich in satire, humor, and frank sensuality, these plays exhibit the underlying corruption and depravity of the sophisticated, glittering surface of Renaissance Italy. The collection includes *La Mandragola*, Machiavelli; *The Faithful Shepherd*, Guarini; *The Deceived*, Gl'Intronati; *Lena*, Ariosto; *The Stablemaster*, Aretino.

448 pp.   0-14-044338-X $ 9.95

Four English Comedies

Edited by J. M. Morrell

Included in this edition are *Valpone*, Jonson; *The Way of the World*, Congreve; *She Stoops to Conquer*, Goldsmith; and *The School for Scandal*, Sheridan.

416 pp.   0-14-043158-6 $ 9.95

The Golden Age of Soviet Theatre

Translated by Max Hayward and Harold Shukman

These three classic plays—*The Bedbug*, Vladimir Mayakovsky; *Marya*, Isaac Babel; and *The Dragon*, Yergeny Schwartz —all written in the twenty years following the Russian Revolution, represent the golden age of Soviet theater.

20TH-CENTURY CLASSICS

224 pp.   0-14-018407-4 $ 7.95

The Government Inspector and Other Russian Plays

Translated and introduced by Joshua Cooper

This collection of the four greatest Russian plays before Chekhov includes *The Government Inspector*, Gogol; *The Infant*, Fonvizin; *Chatsky*, Griboyedov; and *Thunder*, Ostrovsky.

400 pp.   0-14-044579-X $ 9.95

Japanese Nō Dramas

Translated and introduced by Royall Tyler

These twenty-four plays of mesmerizing beauty fuse the spiritual and the sensual in the esoteric Nō art form that combines music, dance, costume, and language. The collection includes full notes and stage directions, as well as new interpretations of the plays which have influenced writers Yeats, Pound, and Brecht.

384 pp.   0-14-044539-0 $ 12.95

Six Yüan Plays

Translated and introduced by Liu Jung-En

Six vibrant plays from the thirteenth century represent the first real Chinese theater to develop free from conservative Confucianism: T*he Orphan of Chao*, *The Soul of Ch'ien-Nü Leaves Her Body*, *The Injustice Done to Tou Ngo*, *Chang Boils the Sea*, *Autumn in Han Palace*, and *A Stratagem of Interlocking Rings*.

288 pp.   0-14-044262-6 $ 9.95

Three Jacobean Tragedies

Edited by Garmini Salgado

From the early seventeenth century, three of the finest examples of Jacobean revenge tragedy make up this collection: *The White Devil* by John Webster, *The Revenger's Tragedy* by Cyril Tourneur, and *The Changeling* by Thomas Middleton and William Rowley.

368 pp.   0-14-043006-7 $ 9.95

Three Restoration Comedies

Edited by Garmini Salgado

This selection includes *The Man of Mode* by Etherege; *The Country Wife* by Wycherley; and *Love for Love* by Congreve.

368 pp.   0-14-043027-X $ 8.95

Two Tudor Tragedies

Edited and introduced by William Tydeman

These two plays—*Gorboduc* and *The Spanish Tragedy*—published for the first time in a single annotated volume, represent Tudor England's fascination with the bloody themes of Greek tragedy and are forerunners of Shakespeare's masterpieces.

368 pp.   0-14-044531-5 $ 10.95

AESCHYLUS
525 B.C.–456 B.C., GREEK

The Oresteia
Agamemnon, The Libation Bearers, The Eumenides

Introduced with notes and glossary by W. B. Stanford
Translated by Robert Fagles

The Oresteia—the only trilogy in Greek drama that survives from antiquity— takes on new depth and power in Robert Fagles's acclaimed modern translation. "The finest Oresteia of all." —*Chronicle of Higher Education*

352 pp.   0-14-044333-9 $ 8.95

The Oresteian Trilogy

Translated by Philip Vellacott

Justice, vengeance, and the forces of fate provide the themes for *Agamemnon*, *The Choephori*, and *The Eumenides*. Philip Vellacott's verse translation is presented with an introduction to Greek mythology, the background of each play, and the historical context of the trilogy.

208 pp.   0-14-044067-4 $ 7.95

Prometheus Bound and Other Plays

Translated by Philip Vellacott

Prometheus Bound, *The Suppliants*, *Seven Against Thebes*, and *The Persians*, presented here in verse translation, examine the struggle between opposing rights or principles.

160 pp.   0-14-044112-3 $ 6.95

ARISTOPHANES
C. 257 B.C.–180 B.C., GREEK

The Frogs and Other Plays

Translated by David Barrett

The role of the poet in Athenian society is explored in three comedies: *The Wasps*, *The Poet and the Women (Thesmophoriazusae)*, and *The Frogs*. This collection includes a general introduction and notes to each play, original line numbers, and stage directions.

256 pp.   0-14-044152-2 $ 9.95

The Knights/The Peace/The Birds/ The Assembly Women/Wealth

Translated by David Barrett and Alan H. Sommerstein

Representing Aristophanes' sharply satirical comedy, this collection is prefaced by an introduction to the history and literary style of the author.

336 pp.   0-14-044332-0 $ 9.95

Lysistrata and Other Plays

Translated and introduced by Alan H. Sommerstein

Three comic plays (*Lysistrata*, *The Acharnians*, and *The Clouds*) reflect the political and social turbulence of Athens during Aristophanes' time.

256 pp.   0-14-044287-1 $ 6.95

BEAUMARCHAIS
1732–1799, FRENCH

The Barber of Seville and The Marriage of Figaro

Translated by John Wood

Known to us almost exclusively through the operas of Rossini and Mozart, these two plays, written with a delightfully light touch, marked high points in eighteenth-century comedy.

224 pp.   0-14-044133-6 $ 7.95

GEORG BÜCHNER
1813–1837, GERMAN

Complete Plays, Lenz and Other Writings

Translated and introduced by John Reddick

Collected in this volume are powerful dramas and psychological fiction by the nineteenth-century iconoclast now recognized as a major figure of world literature. Also included are selections from Büchner's letters and philosophical writings.

368 pp.   0-14-044586-2 $ 10.95

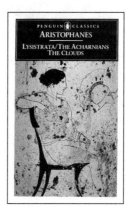

ANTON CHEKHOV
1860–1904, RUSSIAN

Plays

Translated by Elisa veta Fen

Chekhov's realistic and sensitive plays revolve around a society on the brink of tremendous change; included here are *The Cherry Orchard*, *The Seagull*, *Uncle Vania*, *Three Sisters*, and four other plays.

464 pp.   0-14-044096-8 $ 5.95

ARISTOPHANES
c. 257 B.C.–180 B.C., Greek

Aristophanes was an Athenian comic dramatist whose satirical plays were unique in attacking individuals rather than types. He was twice prosecuted for his outspoken attacks on the prominent politician Cleon. His most famous play, and one still performed today, is *Lysistrata,* which discusses government by women. He wrote his first comedy at the age of nineteen and went on to write forty plays; sadly, only eleven of them have survived to the present day.

WILLIAM CONGREVE
1670–1729, ENGLISH

The Comedies of William Congreve
Edited and introduced by Eric S. Rump

Congreve was the most elegant of the Restoration dramatists, and these plays—*The Old Bachelor*, *The Double Dealer*, *Love for Love*, and *The Way of the World*—are wonderfully witty examples of his mastery of the comedy of manners.

416 pp.   0-14-043231-0 $ 10.95

PIERRE CORNEILLE
1606–1684, FRENCH

The Cid, Cinna, The Theatrical Illusion
Translated and introduced by John Cairncross

Corneille's masterpiece, set in medieval Spain, was the first great work of French classical drama; *Cinna*, written three years later in 1641, is a tense political drama, while *The Theatrical Illusion*, an earlier work, is reminiscent of Shakespeare's exuberant comedies.

288 pp.   0-14-044312-6 $ 9.95

EURIPIDES
484 B.C.–406 B.C., GREEK

Alcestis and Other Plays
Translated and introduced by Philip Vellacott

Euripides acts as the skeptical questioner of his age in these verse translations of *Alcestis*, *Hippolytus*, and *Iphigenia in Tauris*.

192 pp.   0-14-044031-3 $ 6.95

The Bacchae and Other Plays
Translated and introduced by Michael Cacoyannis

Four plays—*Ion* and *Helen* in prose, *The Bacchae* and *The Women of Troy* with dialogue rewritten in verse—depict the guilt and suffering of war, and the subsequent loss of faith.

256 pp.   0-14-044044-5 $ 8.95

Medea and Other Plays

Translated by Philip Vellacott

Euripides was the first playwright to use the chorus as commentator, to put contemporary language into the mouths of heroes, and to interpret human suffering without reference to the gods; these verse translations of *Medea*, *Hecuba*, *Electra*, and *Heracles* capture all the brilliance of his work.

208 pp. 0-14-044129-8 $ 7.95

Orestes and Other Plays

Translated and introduced by Philip Vellacott

Spanning the last twenty-four years of Euripides' career, this volume includes *The Children of Heracles*, *Andromache*, *The Suppliant Women*, *The Trojan Women*, *Orestes*, and *Iphigenia in Tauris*.

448 pp. 0-14-044259-6 $ 8.95

JOHN FORD
1586–C. 1639, ENGLISH

Three Plays

Edited and introduced by Keith Sturgess

Sexual tragedy and political failure are uncompromisingly examined in *'Tis Pity She's a Whore*, *The Broken Heart*, and *Perkin Warbeck*, all written during the first half of the seventeenth century.

416 pp. 0-14-043059-8 $ 10.95

JOHN GAY
1685–1732, ENGLISH

The Beggar's Opera

Edited by Bryan Loughrey and T. O. Treadwell
Introduced by Bryan Loughrey

This witty parody of Italian opera, featuring the denizens of the English underworld, was performed more than any other play during the eighteenth century.

128 pp. 0-14-043220-5 $ 7.95

JOHANN W. VON GOETHE
1749–1832, GERMAN

Faust, Part 1

Translated by Philip Wayne

Goethe's masterpiece dramatizes the struggle of modern man to solve the mysteries of energy, pleasure, and the creation of life.

208 pp. 0-14-044012-7 $ 7.95

Faust, Part 2

Translated by Philip Wayne

Rich in allusion and allegory, *Faust, Part 2* was completed a few months before Goethe died and explores philosophical themes that had obsessed him throughout his life.

288 pp. 0-14-044093-3 $ 7.95

HENRIK IBSEN
1828–1906, NORWEGIAN

A Doll's House and Other Plays

Translated by Peter Watts

From *The League of Youth*, his first venture into realistic social drama, to *A Doll's House*, a provocative portrait of a woman's struggle for freedom, to the family tensions depicted in *The Lady from the Sea*, Ibsen is concerned with the individual's conflicts with society.

336 pp.   0-14-044146-8 $ 8.95

Ghosts and Other Plays

Translated by Peter Watts

Incisive, critical, and controversial, *Ghosts* and *An Enemy of the People* depict the negative effects of social rigidity on individual lives; *When We Dead Awaken*, Ibsen's last play, is a story of internal turmoil that can be read as the dramatist's comments on his lifework.

304 pp.   0-14-044135-2 $ 6.95

Hedda Gabler and Other Plays

Translated by Una Ellis-Fermor

The Pillars of the Community and *The Wild Duck* show Ibsen's preoccupation with problems of personal and social morality; *Hedda Gabler*, the latest of these plays, is both a drama of individual conflict and a partial return to social themes.

368 pp.   0-14-044016-X $ 6.95

The Master Builder and Other Plays

Translated by Una Ellis-Fermor

The four plays collected here—*The Master Builder, Rosmersholm, Little Eyolf, John Gabriel Borkman*—were written late in Ibsen's career and reflect his growing interest in internal conflicts and the dangers of self-deception.

384 pp.   0-14-044053-4 $ 7.95

HENRIK IBSEN

1828–1906, Norwegian

Henrik Ibsen was born at Skien, Norway, in 1828. His family went bankrupt when he was a child, and he struggled with poverty for many years. His first ambition was medicine, but he abandoned this to write and to work in theater. A scholarship enabled him to travel to Rome in 1864. In Italy he wrote *Brand* (1866), which earned him a state pension, and *Peer Gynt* (1867), for which Grieg later wrote the incidental music. These plays established his reputation. From *The League of Youth* (1869) onwards, Ibsen renounced poetry and wrote prose drama. He supported in his plays many crucial issues of his day, such as the emancipation of women. Plays like *Ghosts* (1881) and *A Doll's House* (1879) caused a critical uproar.

Peer Gynt

Translated by Peter Watts

This high-spirited poetical fantasy, based on Norwegian folklore, is the story of an irresponsible, lovable hero; after its publication, Ibsen abandoned the verse form for more realistic prose plays.

224 pp.   0-14-044167-0 $ 8.95

BEN JONSON
1572–1637, ENGLISH

Three Comedies

Edited by Michael Jameison

Shakespeare's nearest rival, Jonson created in *Volpone* and *The Alchemist* hilarious portraits of cupidity and chicanery, while in *Bartholomew Fair* he portrays his fellow Londoners at their most festive—and most bawdy.

496 pp.   0-14-043013-X $ 7.95

CHRISTOPHER MARLOWE
1564–1593, ENGLISH

The Complete Plays

Edited by J. B. Steane

Reflecting the remarkable range of this Elizabethan dramatist's interests, this volume contains *Dido, Queen of Carthage, Tamburlaine the Great, Doctor Faustus, The Jew of Malta, Edward the Second*, and *The Massacre at Paris*.

608 pp.   0-14-043037-7 $ 10.95

MENANDER
342 B.C.–292 B.C., GREEK

Plays and Fragments

*Translated and introduced by
Norma Miller*

The most innovative dramatist of the Greek New Comedy period, Menander concentrated on his characters' daily lives and colloquial speech in these comedies of manners. This selection contains all but two of Menander's surviving plays, passages attributed to him, and textual notes.

272 pp.   0-14-044501-3 $ 9.95

CHRISTOPHER MARLOWE

1564–1593, English

Christopher Marlow, the son of a shoemaker, was born in 1564. He was educated at King's School, Canterbury, and received a scholarship to Corpus Christi, Cambridge, where he obtained his B.A. in 1584. Around this time he appears to have been involved in a secret political mission, travelling abroad as a foreign agent. The first part of *Tamburlaine* was performed in 1587 to great acclaim. He wrote the second part the following year and his other great works were written in quick succession. Marlowe brought a bolder tragic conception to that previously seen on the English stage and displayed the real strength and flexibility of blank verse. Marlowe was arrested in May 1593, on charges of blasphemy arising from evidence given by playwright Thomas Kyd. On June 1, 1593, he was stabbed to death in a tavern in Deptford.

THOMAS MIDDLETON
c. 1570–1627, ENGLISH

Five Plays

*Edited and introduced by
Bryan Loughrey and Neil Taylor*

Ranging from ingenious comedy to powerful tragedy, five plays—*A Trick to Catch the Old One*, *The Revenger's Tragedy*, *A Chaste Maid in Cheapside*, *Women Beware Women*, and *The Changeling*—portray the corruptive effects of politics and love in Elizabethan London.

464 pp.   0-14-043219-1 $ 9.95

ARTHUR MILLER
B. 1915, AMERICAN

The Crucible

Based on historical people and real events, Miller's classic play about the witch-hunts and trials in Salem, Massachusetts, is a searing portrait of a community engulfed by hysteria. Readers concerned with the increasing polarization of American society today will discover in *The Crucible* not only a play of extraordinary dramatic intensity, but a provocative reminder of the dangers of imposed moralities and "correct thinking."

20TH-CENTURY CLASSICS

176 pp.   0-14-018964-5 $ 7.95

MOLIÈRE
1622–1673, FRENCH

The Misanthrope and Other Plays

Translated by John Wood

This collection includes *The Misanthrope*, a drama of unrequited love; *Tartuffe*, the first great comedy of obsession; *The Imaginary Invalid*, a burlesque of doctor-patient relationships; *A Doctor in Spite of Himself*, Molière's most famous farce; and *The Sicilian*.

288 pp.   0-14-044089-5 $ 7.95

The Miser and Other Plays

Translated by John Wood

Molière's seventeenth-century comedies set the standard for later comic playwrights; included here are *The Would-Be Gentleman*, *The Miser*, *Don Juan*, *Love's the Best Doctor*, and *That Scoundrel Scapin*.

288 pp.   0-14-044036-4 $ 7.95

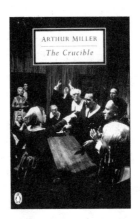

The Pot of Gold
and Other Plays

Translated by E. F. Watling

Plautus's broad humor, reflecting Roman manners and contemporary life, is revealed in these five plays: *The Pot of Gold (Aulularia)*, *The Prisoners (Captivi)*, *The Brothers Menaechmus (Menaechmi)*, *The Swaggering Soldier (Miles Gloriosus)*, and *Pseudolus*.

272 pp.   0-14-044149-2 $ 8.95

The Rope and Other Plays

*Translated and introduced by
E. F. Watling*

This modern translation presents, in a form suitable for the modern stage, *The Ghost (Mostellaria)*, *The Rope (Rudens)*, *A Three-Dollar Day (Trinummus)*, and *Amphitryo*. Also included are an introductory note, list of characters for each play, and stage directions.

288 pp.   0-14-044136-0 $ 9.95

Andromache, Britannicus, Berenice

Translated by John Cairncross

These three works, which brought Racine acclaim with the public and in the court of Louis XIV, are striking examples of how Racine overturned the theatrical conventions of his time by introducing the force of fate into human drama.

288 pp.   0-14-044195-6 $ 8.95

Iphigenia, Phaedra, Athaliah

Translated by John Cairncross

Themes of ruthless and unrelenting tragedy are at the heart of these plays; the first two are based on Greek legend, while Athaliah depicts the vengeance and the power of the Old Testament Jehovah.

320 pp.   0-14-044122-0 $ 7.95

Phèdre

*Translated with a foreword by
Margaret Rawlings*

A favorite among modern readers, students, amateur companies, and repertory theaters alike, Racine's *Phèdre* is the supreme achievement of French neoclassic tragedy. This edition provides both the English and French texts.

192 pp.   0-14-044591-9 $ 8.95

The Robbers and Wallenstein

*Translated and introduced by
F. J. Lamport*

The foremost dramatist of German classicism wrote *The Robbers*, his first play, in 1781; in the trilogy *Wallenstein*, written nineteen years later, Schiller tried to combine the strengths of Sophocles, Shakespeare, and French classical drama.

480 pp.   0-14-044368-1 $ 9.95

Four Tragedies and Octavia

Translated by E. F. Watling

Although their themes are borrowed from Greek drama, these exuberant and often macabre plays focus on action rather than moral concerns and are strikingly different in style from Seneca's prose writing. This collection includes *Phaedra, Oedipus, Thyestes,* and *The Trojan Women.*

320 pp.   0-14-044174-3 $ 10.95

Four Comedies

This collection, including *The Taming of the Shrew, A Midsummer Night's Dream, As You Like It,* and *Twelfth Night* in the New Penguin Shakespeare text, is engagingly introduced and skillfully annotated, and brings together four of Shakespeare's most spirited comedies.

688 pp.   0-14-043454-2 $ 11.95

Four Histories

Shakespeare explores matters of honor and history, tradition and change in this cycle of plays chronicling the turbulent transition of the English monarchy from Richard II through Henry VI.

576 pp.   0-14-043450-X $ 11.95

Four Tragedies

These four tragedies, *Hamlet, Othello, King Lear,* and *Macbeth* in the New Penguin Shakespeare text, contain some of Shakespeare's most celebrated protagonists and finest dramatic poetry.

960 pp.   0-14-043458-5 $ 11.95

Three Roman Plays

Each of these plays, previously published separately in the New Penguin Shakespeare series, investigates political action and the relationship between the personal and the political. Included in this volume are *Coriolanus, Julius Caesar,* and *Antony and Cleopatra.*

672 pp.   0-14-043461-5 $ 11.95

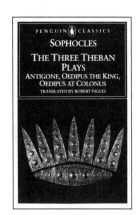

RICHARD BRINSLEY SHERIDAN
1751–1816, IRISH

The School for Scandal and Other Plays

Edited and introduced by Eric S. Rump

Although Sheridan tried his hand at statesmanship, his reputation as a dramatist was enhanced by these three masterpieces of ingenious plotting, eloquent wit, and biting satire. This edition also includes *The Rivals*, his first play, and *The Critic*.

288 pp.   0-14-043240-X $ 8.95

SOPHOCLES
C. 496 B.C.–406 B.C., GREEK

Electra and Other Plays

Translated and introduced by E. F. Watling

These verse translations of four plays exhibit dramatic structure recognizably related to modern decendants: *Ajax*, *Electra*, *The Women of Trachis*, and *Philoctetes*. E. F. Watling discusses the themes of all four dramas and the significance of Sophoclean drama in his introduction, and offers notes to each play.

224 pp.   0-14-044028-3 $ 7.95

The Theban Plays

Translated and introduced by E. F. Watling

Based on the legend of the royal house of Thebes, *King Oedipus*, *Oedipus at Colonus*, and *Antigone* are Sophocles' tragic masterpieces. This verse translation is supplemented by E. F. Watling's introduction, which places Sophocles in historical context, discusses the origins of the art of drama, and interprets each play in the Theban legend.

168 pp.   0-14-044003-8 $ 8.95

The Three Theban Plays
Antigone, Oedipus the King, Oedipus at Colonus

Introduced with notes by Bernard Knox Translated by Robert Fagles

Fagles's lucid modern translation captures the majesty of Sophocles' masterwork, and is enhanced by insightful introductions to each play, an essay on the history of the text, extensive notes, bibliography, and glossary.

432 pp.   0-14-044425-4 $ 8.95

AUGUST STRINDBERG
1849–1912, SWEDISH

Three Plays

Translated by Peter Watts

Combining acute psychological insight and masterful language, Strindberg depicts the war between the sexes in *The Father* and class struggle in *Miss Julie; Easter* is a mystical play, written after Strindberg underwent a religious conversion.

176 pp.   0-14-044082-8 $ 8.95

The Comedies

Translated by Betty Radice

All six of the Roman dramatist's comedies—from *The Girl from Andros*, the first romantic comedy ever written, to the socially sophisticated *The Brothers*—show why Terence became a model for playwrights from the Renaissance onward.

400 pp.   0-14-044324-X $ 9.95

A Month in the Country

Translated and introduced by Isaiah Berlin

Turgenev's most celebrated play, written in 1850, is a tragicomedy exploring that most universal theme the love triangle.

128 pp.   0-14-044436-X $ 7.95

Three Plays

Introduced with notes by D. C. Dunby

Often compared to Shakespeare, Webster was renowned in his day and beyond. This sampling of his plays features *The White Devil*, *The Duchess of Malfi*, and *The Devil's Law-Case*.

464 pp.   0-14-043081-4 $ 9.95

The Economic Consequences of the Peace

Introduced by Robert Lekachman

One of the great economic and political works of our time, Keynes's brilliant and prescient analysis of the economic effects of the Treaty of Versailles offers vehement opposition to a reparations policy that would stifle the German economy in the aftermath of World War I.

20TH-CENTURY CLASSICS
336 pp.   0-14-018805-3 $ 12.95

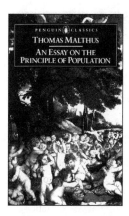

THOMAS ROBERT MALTHUS
1766–1834, ENGLISH

An Essay on the Principle of Population

Edited by Antony Flew

In a thesis that explores the disparity between the potential rates of growth of population and of the means of subsistence, Malthus presents the ultimate demographic choice: starvation or restraint.

304 pp.   0-14-043206-X $ 8.95

BERNARD MANDEVILLE
1670–1733, DUTCH

The Fable of the Bees

Edited and translated by Philip Harth

This masterpiece of eighteenth-century English satire sparked great social controversy by rejecting a positive view of human nature and arguing the necessity of vice as the foundation of an emerging capitalist economy.

416 pp.   0-14-044541-2 $ 10.95

KARL MARX
1818–1883, GERMAN

Capital
Volume 1, Volume 2, Volume 3

For a description, see HISTORY AND POLITICS.

Grundrisse
Foundations of the Critique of Political Economy

Translated with a foreword by Martin Nickolaus

Written between *The Communist Manifesto* (1848) and the first volume of *Capital* (1867), the *Grundrisse*—essential to the understanding of Marx's ideas—provides the only outline of his full political-economic theories.

912 pp.   0-14-044575-7 $ 15.95

JOHN STUART MILL
1806–1873, ENGLISH

Principles of Political Economy

Edited and introduced by Donald Winch

This volume contains the two concluding books of Mill's durable classic—"Influence of the Progress of Society on Production and Distribution" and "On the Influence of Government," as well as important passages regarding socialism and the distribution of property.

400 pp.   0-14-043260-4 $ 10.95

ADAM SMITH
1723–1790, SCOTTISH

The Wealth of Nations
Books I–III

*Edited and introduced by
Andrew Skinner*

In this work, which laid the foundations
of economic theory in general and of
"classical" economics in particular,
Adam Smith pinpointed the division
of labor as a major explanation of
economic growth.

544 pp.   0-14-043208-6 $ 7.95

THORSTEIN VEBLEN
1857–1929, AMERICAN

The Theory of the Leisure Class

This classic of economic thought and so-
ciology was conceived by a writer
C. Wright Mills has called "the best critic
of America that America has produced."

20TH-CENTURY CLASSICS

144 pp.   0-14-018795-2 $ 9.95

HISTORY AND POLITICS

Alfred the Great

*Translated by Simon Keynes and
Michael Lapidge*

This comprehensive collection includes
Asser's *Life of Alfred;* extracts from *The
Anglo-Saxon Chronicle;* and Alfred's
own writings, laws, and will.

368 pp.   0-14-044409-2 $ 11.95

Ancrene Wisse
Guide for Anchoresses

For a description, see RELIGION.

Colonial American Travel Narratives

Edited by Wendy Martin

Four different journeys by early Americans Mary Rowlandson, Sarah Kemble
Knight, William Byrd II, and Dr. Alexander Hamilton recount the vivid physical and psychological challenges of
colonial life. Essential primary texts in
the study of early American cultural life,
they are now collected in one single volume.

336 pp.   0-14-039088-X $ 11.95

Divine Right and Democracy
An Anthology of Political Writing in Stuart England
Edited by David Wooton

Reflecting the political debate that characterized England's century of revolution, these thirty-three thematically arranged selections prefigure modern conceptions of political rights and social change. The volume includes speeches, essays, and polemical pamphlets from anonymous writers as well as from James VI and James I, Sir John Davies, John Lilburne, Charles I, Richard Hooker, Roger Williams, Gerrard Winstanley, Robert Sanderson, Francis Bacon, Algernon Sidney, John Locke, Bernard Mandeville, and others.

512 pp.   0-14-043250-7 $ 10.95

Early American Writing
Edited and introduced by Giles Gunn

This panoramic collection, drawn from original documents of early American life and literature, brings together an extraordinary diversity of voices—black, white, Hispanic, Native, French, male and female.

720 pp.   0-14-039087-1 $ 12.95

The Federalist Papers
Edited and introduced by
Isaac Kramnick

The definitive exposition of the American Constitution, *The Federalist Papers* were considered by Thomas Jefferson to be the best commentary on the principle of government ever written. This collection of all eighty-five papers contains the complete first-edition text of the collected essays published in 1787–1788 in New York by J. and A. McLean. Includes the U.S. Constitution.

528 pp.   0-14-044495-5 $ 10.95

Greek Political Oratory
Edited, selected, translated, and
introduced by A. N. W. Saunders

These fifteen representative orations made by Thucydides, Lysias, Andocides, Isocrates, and Demosthenes highlight the Greek mastery of speech, history, and philosophy that marked the years between 510 B.C. and 336 B.C.

272 pp.   0-14-044223-5 $ 9.95

Hippocratic Writings
Edited by G. E. R. Lloyd
Translated by J. Chadwick, W. N. Mann,
E. T. Withington, and I. M. Lonie

These writings by Hippocrates and other medical pioneers reveal the origins of Western medicine and the ideal of ethical practice, as well as the origin of the scientific method.

384 pp.   0-14-044451-3 $ 9.95

Lives of the Later Caesars

*Translated and introduced by
Anthony Birley*

This edition contains the first part of
the Augustan history, the only true sequel to Suetonius's *The Twelve Caesars*,
covering the emperors from Hadrian to
Heliogabalus (A.D. 117–222).

336 pp.   0-14-044308-8 $ 9.95

HENRY ADAMS
1838–1918, AMERICAN

The Education of Henry Adams

Edited and introduced by Jean Gooder

Adams examines the progress of America from the Civil War period to the nation's ascendancy as a world power,
attempting to understand what sustains
societies and what destroys them. A
remarkable synthesis of history, art,
politics, philosophy, and science, *The
Education of Henry Adams* remains a
provocative and stimulating interpretation of the birth of the twentieth century.

608 pp.   0-14-044557-9 $ 11.95

HANNAH ARENDT
1906–1975, GERMAN

Eichmann in Jerusalem
A Report on the Banality of Evil

Arendt's authoritative report (1963) on
the trial of Nazi leader Adolph Eich-
mann deals with the problem of the human being within a modern totalitarian
system, called by Bruno Bettelheim "the
greatest problem of our time." This
posthumous revised edition contains a
postscript by Arendt, and further fac-
tual material revealed after the trial.

20TH-CENTURY CLASSICS

320 pp.   0-14-018765-0 $ 11.95

On Revolution

This lucid analysis of a relatively recent
political phenomenon examines the
principles that underlie all revolutions;
discusses three classic revolutions—the
American, the French, and the Russian;
and shows how both the theory and
practice of revolution have developed.

20TH-CENTURY CLASSICS

352 pp.   0-14-018421-X $ 10.95

ARRIAN
2ND CENT. A.D., GREEK

The Campaigns of Alexander

Translated by Aubrey de Sélincourt

Although written four hundred years
after Alexander's death, Arrian's *Campaigns of Alexander*, is the most reliable
account of the conqueror's life.

432 pp.   0-14-044253-7 $ 10.95

JACOB BURCKHARDT
1818–1897, SWISS

The Civilization of the Renaissance in Italy

Translated by S. G. C. Middlemore
Introduced by Peter Burke

In this classic nineteenth-century historical work, Burckhardt explores the political and psychological forces that marked the Renaissance as the beginning of the modern world.

416 pp.   0-14-044534-X $ 10.95

BEDE
C. 673–735, ENGLISH

The Age of Bede

Edited by D. H. Farmer
Translated by J. F. Webb and D. H. Farmer

Four of the finest medieval hagiographies provide valuable insight into the religious life and thought of the period. This collection includes *The Voyage of St. Brendan, Bede's Life of Cuthbert, Lives of the Abbots of Wearmouth and Jarrow*, and Eddius Stephanus's *Life of Wilfrid*.

256 pp.   0-14-044437-8 $ 8.95

Ecclesiastical History of the English People

Edited and introduced by D. H. Farmer
Translated by Leo Sherley-Price

Opening with a background sketch of Roman Britain's geography and history, Bede recounts the development of the Anglo-Saxon government and religion during the formative years of the English people.

400 pp.   0-14-044565-X $ 9.95

EDMUND BURKE
1729–1797, IRISH

Reflections on the Revolution in France

Edited and introduced by Conor Cruise O'Brien

The great debate on the French Revolution was touched off by *Reflections*, which reveals Burke as a much more radical—even revolutionary—thinker than admitted by those who view him as the father of modern conservatism.

400 pp.   0-14-043204-3 $ 6.95

JULIUS CAESAR
100 B.C.–44 B.C., ROMAN

The Civil War

Translated by Jane F. Gardner

The Civil War, together with accounts of the Alexandrian, African, and Spanish wars (probably written by Caesar's lieutenants), portrays Caesar's struggle for power.

360 pp.   0-14-044187-5 $ 8.95

The Conquest of Gaul

Translated by S. A. Hanford

Caesar's account of the Gallic Wars, although based on fact, also served to impress his contemporaries and justify himself to his enemies. This edition restores the traditional order of the work and incorporates into the text information previously included as footnotes.

288 pp.   0-14-044433-5 $ 8.95

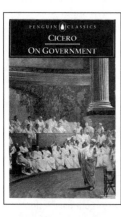

CHARLES W. CHESNUTT
1858–1932, AMERICAN

The Marrow of Tradition

For a description, see LITERATURE.

MARCUS TULLIUS CICERO
106 B.C.–43 B.C., ROMAN

Murder Trials

Translated by Michael Grant

Cicero's speeches "In Defence of Sextus Roscius of Amerina," "In Defence of Aulus Cluentius Habitus," "In Defence of Gaius Rabirius," "Note on the Speeches in Defence of Caelius and Milo," and "In Defence of King Deiotarus" provide insight into Roman life, law, and history.

368 pp.   0-14-044288-X $ 10.95

On Government

Translated and introduced by Michael Grant

These pioneering writings on the mechanics, tactics, and strategies of government were devised by the Roman Republic's most enlightened thinker.

432 pp.   0-14-044595-1 $ 11.95

Selected Letters

Translated and introduced by D. R. Shakleton Bailey

Peopled by legends ranging from Pompey, Caesar, and Brutus to Cassius and Mark Antony, this selection of thirteen letters chosen from Volumes 1 and 2 of Cicero's *Letters to His Friends* chronicles the political and social life of a dying civilization.

288 pp.   0-14-044458-0 $ 10.95

Selected Political Speeches

Translated by Michael Grant

The seven speeches in this volume, annotated to supply the relevant political history of the period, include the speeches against the Catilinarian conspiracy as well as the first "Philippic" against Mark Antony.

336 pp.   0-14-044214-6 $ 9.95

Selected Works

Translated by Michael Grant

Divided into two parts—"Against Tyranny" and "How to Live"—this selection of Cicero's work reveals the private and public sides of his liberal personality and his opposition to oppressive and unparliamentary methods of government.

272 pp.   0-14-044099-2 $ 8.95

CARL VON CLAUSEWITZ
1730–1831, PRUSSIAN

On War

*Edited and introduced by
Anatol Rapoport*

Written in 1832, this treatise presents the great Prussian soldier's views on both total war and war as a continuation of politics.

464 pp.   0-14-044427-0 $ 9.95

CHRISTOPHER COLUMBUS
1451–1506, SPANISH

The Four Voyages

Translated by J. M. Cohen

This enthralling volume includes Columbus's letters and logbook and remains the definitive primary source on his voyages to Cuba, Haiti/Hispaniola, Jamaica, Trinidad, and the Central American mainland.

320 pp.   0-14-044217-0 $ 8.95

ANNA COMNENA
1083–C. 1148, BYZANTINE

The Alexiad of Anna Comnena

Translated by E. R. A. Sewter

A Byzantine emperor's daughter vividly records the turbulence that marked the rule of her father, Alexius I (1081–1118).

560 pp.   0-14-044215-4 $ 10.95

J. HECTOR ST. JOHN DE CRÈVECOEUR
1735–1813, FRENCH

Letters from an American Farmer and Sketches of Eighteenth-Century America

Edited and introduced by Albert E. Stone

America's physical and cultural landscape is captured in these two classics of American history. *Letters* provides an invaluable view of the pre-Revolutionary and Revolutionary eras; *Sketches* details in vivid prose the physical setting in which American settlers created their history.

496 pp.   0-14-039006-5 $ 8.95

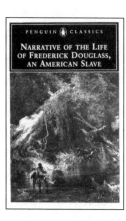

PENGUIN CLASSICS

NARRATIVE OF THE LIFE
OF FREDERICK DOUGLASS,
AN AMERICAN SLAVE

FREDERICK DOUGLASS
1817–1895, AMERICAN

Narrative of the Life of Frederick Douglass, an American Slave
Written by Himself

*Edited and introduced by
Houston A. Baker, Jr.*

The pre-eminent example of the American slave narrative, Douglass's personal account of life in the pre–Civil War American South is a telling indictment of the institution of slavery and of the people and the country that allowed it to flourish.

160 pp.   0-14-039012-X $ 6.95

BERNAL DÍAZ
1492–C. 1581, SPANISH

The Conquest of New Spain
Translated by J. M. Cohen

Drawing on his experience as a Spanish soldier in Cortez's army, Díaz provides the classic eyewitness account of Cortez's war against the Aztecs.

416 pp.   0-14-044123-9 $ 9.95

CASSIUS DIO
C. 150–C. 235, ROMAN

The Roman History
The Reign of Augustus

Translated by Ian Scott-Kilvert

Following Rome's long road to peace after decades of civil war, Cassius Dio provides the fullest account of the reign of the first emperor in Books 50 through 60 of his Roman history.

336 pp.   0-14-044448-3 $ 10.95

W. E. B. DUBOIS
1868–1963, AMERICAN

The Souls of Black Folk
Introduced by Donald B. Gibson

Social reformer and activist W. E. B. DuBois expresses his passionate concern for the future of his race in this 1903 collection of essays depicting the psychological effects of segregation on American society. This important social document attempts to improve relations not only between blacks and whites but among blacks themselves.

224 pp.   0-14-039074-X $ 9.95

ERASMUS OF ROTTERDAM
c. 1466–1536, Dutch

Erasmus was the greatest of the Renaissance humanists. *Praise of Folly* is both his best-known work and the best introduction to his thought. Although Erasmus claimed it was written in a week to amuse Sir Thomas More, the dazzling display of playful paradoxes and learned high spirits cannot disguise a far deeper purpose. *Folly* starts by criticizing everything her creator held dear, and celebrating youth, pleasure, drunkenness, and the dizzying sexual desires that created us all. Later sections examine human pretensions, foibles, and frailties, mock theologians and monks, and praise the "folly" of simple Christian piety. Erasmus's wit, wisdom, and mastery of tone made this book an instant but controversial success; the *Letter to Maarten van Dorp,* a lively defense of his ideas and methods, is also included here.

Chronicles

Selected, introduced, and translated by Geoffrey Brereton

This selection from Froissart's *Chronicles* forms a vast panorama of Europe, from the deposition of Edward II to the downfall of Richard II.

496 pp.   0-14-044200-6 $ 10.95

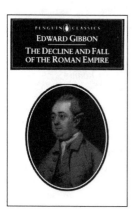

The History of the Kings of Britain

Translated and introduced by Lewis Thorpe

This heroic epic of the twelfth century, describing such half-legendary kings as Cymbeline, Arthur, and Lear, inspired Malory, Spenser, Shakespeare, and many other writers.

384 pp.   0-14-044170-0 $ 9.95

The History and Topography of Ireland

Translated by John O'Meara

Arguably the most authoritative primary source for what is known about medieval Ireland, this lively history by a twelfth-century Norman describes the land's topography, natural resources, and inhabitants in vivid detail. Maps.

144 pp.   0-14-044423-8 $ 9.95

The Journey Through Wales, The Description of Wales

Translated and introduced by Lewis Thorpe

The Journey, an accurate and comprehensive history of twelfth-century Wales, is filled with lively anecdotes and folklore; *The Description* offers a fascinating picture of the life of ordinary Welshmen.

336 pp.   0-14-044339-8 $ 10.95

The Decline and Fall of the Roman Empire

Edited and introduced by Dero A. Saunders

Gibbon's great historical masterpiece is condensed and combined with a summary of the deleted materials.

704 pp.   0-14-043189-6 $ 11.95

WILLIAM GODWIN
1756–1836, ENGLISH

An Enquiry Concerning Political Justice
And Its Influence on Modern Morals and Happiness

Edited and introduced by Isaac Kramnick

The Enquiry, first published in 1793, established the author as the chief exponent of British radicalism—a tradition which calls for the establishment of rational anarchy to liberate the individual from the "brute engine" of oppressive forms of government and the rule of law and order.

848 pp.   0-14-040030-3 $ 11.95

GREGORY OF TOURS
538–594, FRANKISH

A History of the Franks

Translated by Lewis Thorpe

This colorful narrative of French history in the sixth century is a dramatic and detailed portrait of a period of political and religious turmoil.

720 pp.   0-14-044295-2 $ 9.95

RICHARD HAKLUYT
C. 1552–1616, ENGLISH

Voyages and Discoveries

Edited, abridged, and introduced by Jack Beeching

In Renaissance diplomat, scholar, and spy Richard Hakluyt's work lie the beginnings of geography, economics, ethnography, and the modern world itself.

442 pp.   0-14-043073-3 $ 9.95

HERODOTUS
C. 484 B.C.–C. 435 B.C., GREEK

The Histories

Revised and introduced by A. R. Burn
Translated by Aubrey de Sélincourt

The first great prose work in European literature records the struggle between Europe and Asia, culminating in the invasion of Greece by Xerxes.

656 pp.   0-14-044034-8 $ 8.95

EDWARD GIBBON
1737–1794, English

Gibbon was born in 1737, in Putney, and was the only child of his parents to survive infancy. Although his education was frequently interrupted by ill health, his knowledge was far-reaching. His brief career as an undergraduate at Magdalen College, Oxford, ended when he joined the Catholic Church. It was while he was in Rome in 1764 that he first conceived the work that was eventually to become *The History of the Decline and Fall of the Roman Empire*. The first volume was published in 1776; it was highly praised for its learning and for its style but incurred some censure for the comments on the Early Christians. The second and third volumes appeared in 1781 and the final three in 1788.

THOMAS HOBBES
1588–1679, ENGLISH

Leviathan

Edited by C. B. Macpherson

Written amid the turmoil of the English civil war, Hobbes's apologia for the emergent seventeenth-century mercantile society speaks directly to twentieth-century minds in its concern for peace, systematic analysis of power, and elevation of politics to the status of a science.

736 pp.   0-14-043195-0 $ 8.95

JEAN DE JOINVILLE and GEOFFROI DE VILLEHARDOUIN
C. 1224–1317; C. 1150–1213 FRENCH

Chronicles of the Crusade

Translated by M. R. B. Shaw

These two famous Old French chronicles were composed by soldiers who took part in the Holy Wars and offer both eyewitness accounts of the battles and a picture of life in the East.

368 pp.   0-14-044124-7 $ 11.95

FLAVIUS JOSEPHUS
C. 37–C. 100, JEWISH HISTORIAN

The Jewish War
Revised Edition

*Revised and introduced by
E. Mary Smallwood
Translated by G. A. Williamson*

Josephus depicts in vivid detail the Jewish rebellion of A.D. 66, supplying much of the available information on first-century Palestine.

512 pp.   0-14-044420-3 $ 10.95

JUSTINIAN
483–565, ROMAN

The Digest of Roman Law
Theft, Rapine, Damage, and Insult

*Translated and introduced by
C. F. Kolbert*

Codified by Justinian I and published under his aegis in A.D. 533, this celebrated work of legal history forms a fascinating picture of ordinary life in Rome.

192 pp.   0-14-044343-6 $ 9.95

JOHN MAYNARD KEYNES
1883–1946, ENGLISH

The Economic Consequences of the Peace

For a description, see ECONOMICS.

BARTOLOMÉ DE LAS CASAS
1484–1576, SPANISH

A Short Account of the Destruction of the Indies

*Introduced by Anthony Pagden
Translated by Nigel Griffin*

No work is a stronger, more exacting, more heartbreaking record of the Spanish atrocities in the genocidal enterprise of colonization in the Americas. This account provides an eyewitness's history of the process in the territory of Columbus.

192 pp.   0-14-044562-5 $ 9.95

The State and Revolution

Translated and introduced by
Robert Service

In this seminal work of Soviet literature
and Bolshevism, Lenin calls for the destruction of the bourgeoisie and capitalism and the establishment of a new
post-revolutionary order.

20TH-CENTURY CLASSICS

192 pp.   0-14-018435-X $ 11.95

What Is to Be Done?

Introduced by Robert Service
Translated by Joe Fineberg and
George Hanna

One of the definitive statements of
Marxism-Leninism, *What Is to Be
Done?* sets forth Lenin's ideas about
party organization, structure, and essential communist theory and practice.

20TH-CENTURY CLASSICS

262 pp.   0-14-018126-1 $ 9.95

Moments of Reprieve

For a description, see AUTOBIOGRAPHY
AND BIOGRAPHY.

The Early History of Rome

Introduced by R. M. Ogilvie
Translated by Aubrey de Sélincourt

The first five books of Livy's monumental *History of Rome* trace the foundation
of Rome through the Gallic invasion of
the fourth century B.C.

424 pp.   0-14-044104-2 $ 9.95

Rome and Italy

Translated and annotated by
Betty Radice

Books VI to X of Livy's *History of Rome*
cover a dramatic century—from Rome's
apparent collapse after defeat by the
Gauls in 386 B.C. to its emergence as the
premier power in Italy in 293 B.C.

400 pp.   0-14-044388-6 $ 9.95

Rome and the Mediterranean

Introduced by A. H. McDonald
Translated by Henry Bettenson

Books XXXI to XLV of Livy's *History of
Rome* cover the years from 201 B.C. to
167 B.C., when Rome emerged as ruler
of the Mediterranean.

704 pp.   0-14-044318-5 $ 12.95

The War with Hannibal

Introduced by Betty Radice
Translated by Aubrey de Sélincourt

Books XXI to XXX of Livy's *History of
Rome* cover the declaration of the Second Punic War in 218 B.C. to the battle
in 202 B.C. at Zama in Africa, where
Hannibal was finally defeated.

712 pp.   0-14-044145-X $ 9.95

THOMAS BABINGTON MACAULAY
1800–1859, ENGLISH

The History of England

Edited, abridged, and introduced by Hugh Trevor-Roper

Macaulay's monumental *History* covers the period from the accession of James II through the 1688 revolution and up to the death of William III.

576 pp.   0-14-043133-0 $ 10.95

NICCOLÒ MACHIAVELLI
1469–1527, ITALIAN

The Discourses

Edited and introduced by Bernard Crick
Revised by Brain Richardson
Translated by Leslie J. Walker

Machiavelli examines the glorious republican past of Rome. In contrast with *The Prince,* this unfinished work upholds the republic as the best and most enduring style of government.

544 pp.   0-14-044428-9 $ 8.95

The Prince

Translated and introduced by George Bull

This famous treatise on statecraft expounds Machiavelli's principles for building a government that will last—stating uncompromisingly what most governments do but none profess to do. 🖥

160 pp.   0-14-044107-7 $ 4.50

AMMIANUS MARCELLINUS
C. 4TH CENT., ROMAN

The Later Roman Empire
(A.D. 354–378)

Introduced with notes by Andrew Wallace Hadrill
Translated by Walter Hamilton

Considered to be the last great Roman historian, Marcellinus continues the histories of Tacitus, describing the reigns of the emperors Constantius, Julian, Jovian, Valentinian, and Valens.

512 pp.   0-14-044406-8 $ 12.95

KARL MARX
1818–1883, GERMAN

Capital
Volume 1

Translated by Ben Fowkes

This 1867 study—one of the most influential documents of modern times—looks at the relationship between labor and value, the role of money, and the conflict between the classes.

1,152 pp.   0-14-044568-4 $ 14.95

Capital
Volume 2

Introduced by Ernest Mandel
Translated by David Fernbach

The "forgotten" second volume of *Capital,* Marx's world-shaking analysis of economics, politics, and history, contains the vital discussion of commodity, cornerstone to Marx's theories.

624 pp.   0-14-044569-2 $ 13.95

Capital
Volume 3

Introduced by Ernest Mandel
Translated by David Fernbach

The third volume of the book that changed the course of world history, *Capital*'s final chapters were Marx's most controversial writings on the subject, and were never completed.

1,088 pp.   0-14-044570-6 $ 14.95

Early Writings

Translated by Gregor Benton and Rodney Livingstone

In this rich body of early work the foundations of Marxism can be seen in essays on alienation, the state, democracy, and human nature.

464 pp.   0-14-044574-9 $ 10.95

The First International and After
Political Writings: Volume 3

Edited and introduced by David Fernbach

In this third volume of the collection, Marx applies the pioneering insights of *Capital* to ongoing international events, and foresees the possibilty of revolution in Russia.

432 pp.   0-14-044573-0 $ 11.95

Grundrisse
Foundations of the Critique of Political Economy

For a description, see ECONOMICS.

The Revolutions of 1848
Political Writings: Volume 1

Edited and introduced by David Fernbach

The first of a three-volume collection of the political writings of Karl Marx, *The Revolutions* is a study of the failed European revolutions, and Marx's call for an independent workers' organization to begin the "permanent revolution." Includes the *Manifesto of the Communist Party*.

368 pp.   0-14-044571-4 $ 10.95

Surveys from Exile
Political Writings: Volume 2

Edited and introduced by David Fernbach

This second volume contains essays written by Marx at mid-century during a period of isolation and political inactivity. It includes writings on the Crimean War, the American Civil War, India, China, and more, and foreshadows ideas in his *Capital*.

384 pp.   0-14-044572-2 $ 10.95

KARL MARX and FRIEDRICH ENGELS
1818–1883, GERMAN
1820–1895, GERMAN

The Communist Manifesto

Introduced by A. J. P. Taylor

This compelling document by any standard is even more relevant today in light of the recent downfall of communism. It includes a special introduction by the noted British historian A. J. P. Taylor.

128 pp.   0-14-044478-5 $ 5.95

HENRY MAYHEW
1812–1887, ENGLISH

London Labour and the London Poor

Selected and introduced by Victor Neuburg

These true scenes of life among Victorian London's lowest classes—detailed, unsentimental, and remarkably free of sociopolitical cant—are among the most shocking ever depicted.

544 pp.   0-14-043241-8 $ 10.95

JOHN STUART MILL
1806–1873, ENGLISH

On Liberty

Edited and introduced by Gertrude Himmelfarb

Dedicated to the principle of the personal sovereignty of the individual, Mill's most famous work still stands as an essential treatise on the subject of human liberty.

192 pp.   0-14-043207-8 $ 7.95

MICHEL DE MONTAIGNE
1533–1592, FRENCH

An Apology for Raymond Sebond

Translated and introduced by M. A. Screech

A masterpiece of Counter-Reformation and Renaissance argument, Montaigne's *Apology* is a witty defense of natural theology and an eloquent expression of Christian skepticism.

240 pp.   0-14-044493-9 $ 9.95

THOMAS MORE
1478–1535, ENGLISH

Utopia

Translated by Paul Turner

Utopia revolutionized Plato's classic blueprint for the perfect republic—later seen as a source of Anabaptism, Mormonism, and even communism.

160 pp.   0-14-044165-4 $ 5.95

ROBERT OWEN
1771–1858, WELSH

A New View of Society and Other Writings

Edited and introduced by Gregory Claeys

This wide-ranging selection of Owen's writings reflects his intense concern for equality and justice, education, and labor reform, and offers insights into his radical proposal for a full-scale reorganization of British society through the concept of cooperative model communities.

416 pp.   0-14-043348-1 $ 11.95

THOMAS PAINE
1737–1809, AMERICAN

Common Sense

Edited and introduced by
Isaac Kramnick

Published anonymously in 1776, *Common Sense* was instrumental in initiating the movement that established the independence of the United States. Drawn from Paine's experience of revolutionary politics, this treatise formulates the principles of fundamental human rights later expounded in *The Rights of Man*.

128 pp.   0-14-039016-2 $ 6.95

The Rights of Man

Introduced by Eric Foner

Written in reply to Burke's *Reflections on the Revolution in France*, Paine's *Rights of Man* enshrines the radical attitude in its purest form.

288 pp.   0-14-039015-4 $ 8.95

The Thomas Paine Reader

Edited and introduced by Michael Foot
and Isaac Kramnick

This collection focuses on Paine as the political theorist who was an inspiration to Americans in their struggle for independence, as a great defender of individual rights, and as the most incendiary of English radical writers.

544 pp.   0-14-044496-3 $ 10.95

THOMAS PAINE
1737–1809, American

Thomas Paine was born in England in 1737. After a school career that ended at age thirteen, a series of obscure jobs and two failed marriages, he emigrated to Philadelphia in 1774 at Benjamin Franklin's suggestion. Within fourteen months he had published the pamphlet *Common Sense*. He continued his journalistic career with an essay series, *The American Crisis*, which includes the famous passage beginning, "These are the times that try men's souls," which Washington ordered read to his troops before the Battle of Trenton. John Adams once said that history would "ascribe the American Revolution to Paine," but Paine's involvement with the French Revolution, during which he was imprisoned and nearly executed, was seen by many as advocating anarchy. That revolutionary stance and his most controversial work, *The Age of Reason*, which was considered atheistic, led to his repudiation by his former supporters. He died following years of poverty and ill health in 1802.

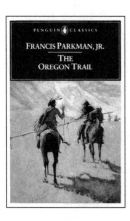

The Oregon Trail

Edited and introduced by David Levin

On April 28, 1846, Francis Parkman left Saint Louis for his first expedition west. *The Oregon Trail* documents his adventures in the wilderness, sheds light on America's westward expansion, and celebrates the American spirit.

500 pp.   0-14-039042-1 $ 9.95

Guide to Greece

Translated and introduced by Peter Levi

Pausanias' classic account of every Greek city and sanctuary includes historical introductions and a record of local customs and beliefs. Volume 1 covers central Greece, the country around Athens, Delphi, and Mycenae; Volume 2 describes southern Greece, including Olympia, Sparta, Arcadia, and Bassae.

Vol. 1: 592 pp. 0-14-044225-1 $ 12.95
Vol. 2: 544 pp. 0-14-044226-X $ 12.95

The Treasure of the City of the Ladies
Or The Book of Three Virtues

Translated and introduced by Sarah Lawson

A valuable counterbalance to chronicles of medieval life written by men, this 1405 "survival manual" addresses all women, from those at the royal court to prostitutes, and portrays their lives in fine and often wry detail.

192 pp.   0-14-044453-X $ 8.95

Natural History

Translated and introduced by John F. Healey

This encyclopedic account of the state of science, art, and technology in the first century A.D. also provides a substantial volume of evidence about Pliny's character, temperament, and attitude toward life. Including more than 20,000 facts—from agriculture, astronomy, botany, and chemistry to geography, pharmacy, and zoology—this work is the major source of ancient beliefs about every form of useful knowledge.

448 pp.   0-14-044413-0 $ 11.95

PLINY THE YOUNGER
C. 62–C. 113, ROMAN

The Letters of the Younger Pliny

*Translated and introduced by
Betty Radice*

This modern translation of the ten books of Pliny's *Letters* provides a wealth of information on the social and political history of Rome at the turn of the first century, including Pliny's famous account of the destruction of Pompeii and his celebrated correspondence with the Emperor Trajan about the early Christians.

320 pp.   0-14-044127-1 $ 9.95

PLUTARCH
C. 46–C. 119, GREEK

The Age of Alexander

*Introduced by G. T. Griffith
Translated and annotated by
Ian Scott-Kilvert*

Taken from the *Parallel Lives*, this history of nine great Greek statesmen—Agesilaus, Pelopidas, Dion, Timoleon, Demosthenes, Phocion, Alexander, Demetrius, and Pyrrhus—traces a crucial phase of ancient history, from the fall of Athens to the rise of Macedonia.

448 pp.   0-14-044286-3 $ 9.95

Essays

*Edited and introduced by Ian Kidd
Translated by Robin Waterfield*

Twenty centuries after they were written, Plutarch's essays resound with his charm, his classical wisdom, and his humanism.

448 p.   0-14-044564-1 $ 11.95

The Fall of the Roman Republic

*Introduced with notes by Robin Seager
Translated by Rex Warner*

Selections on Gaius, Marius, Sulla, Crassus, Pompey, Caesar, and Cicero are taken from the Parallel Lives. Plutarch records, simply and dramatically, the long and bloody period of foreign and civil war that marked the collapse of the Roman Republic and ushered in the Empire.

368 pp.   0-14-044084-4 $ 10.95

Makers of Rome

*Translated and introduced by
Ian Scott-Kilvert*

Nine of Plutarch's Roman lives—Coriolanus, Fabius Maximus, Marcellus, Cato the Elder, Tiberius Gracchus, Gaius Gracchus, Sertorius, Brutus, and Mark Antony—illustrate the courage and tenacity of the Romans in war and their genius for political compromise, from the earliest years of the Republic to the establishment of the Empire.

368 pp.   0-14-044158-1 $ 9.95

Plutarch on Sparta

Translated by Richard J. A. Talbert

Rich in anecdote and personal idiosyncrasy, Plutarch's writings are a literary, philosophical, and social exploration of this extraordinary Greek city.

224 pp.   0-14-044463-7 $ 9.95

The Rise and Fall of Athens

Translated by Ian Scott-Kilvert

Nine Greek biographies illustrate the rise and fall of Athens, from the legendary days of Theseus, the city's founder, through Solon, Themistocles, Aristides, Cimon, Pericles, Nicias, and Alcibiades, to the razing of its walls by Lysander.

320 pp.   0-14-044102-6 $ 8.95

POLYBIUS
C. 200 B.C.–C. 118 B.C., GREEK

The Rise of the Roman Empire

Introduced by F. W. Walbank
Translated by Ian Scott-Kilvert

The forty books of Polybius's *Universal History*, by covering events in the third and second centuries B.C. that led to the supremacy of Rome, present the first panoramic view of history.

576 pp.   0-14-044362-2 $ 10.95

PROCOPIUS
6TH CENT., BYZANTINE

The Secret History

Translated and introduced by
G. A. Williamson

The other side of sixth-century Byzantium is revealed as Procopius exposes the vicious, scheming nature of the splendid empire and its rulers.

208 pp.   0-14-044182-4 $ 9.95

MICHAEL PSELLUS
1018–C. 1078, BYZANTINE

Fourteen Byzantine Rulers

Introduced by Joan Hussey
Translated by E. R. A. Sewter

This chronicle of the Byzantine Empire, beginning in 1025, shows a profound understanding of power politics that characterized the empire and led to its decline.

400 pp.   0-14-044169-7 $ 10.95

JOHN REED
1887–1920, AMERICAN

Ten Days That Shook the World

Introduced by A. J. P. Taylor and
V. I. Lenin

Reed's classic eyewitness account of the events in Petrograd in November of 1917 "rises above every other contemporary record" (George F. Kennan).

20TH-CENTURY CLASSICS

368 pp.   0-14-018293-4 $ 7.95

QUINTUS CURTIUS RUFUS
C. 1ST CENT., ROMAN

The History of Alexander

Translated and introduced by
John Yardley and Waldemar Heckel

The only life of Alexander in Latin, this highly literary account complements Arrian's *Campaigns of Alexander*, drawing on a wide variety of questionable as well as trustworthy sources to paint a portrait of the personal side of the conqueror.

352 pp.   0-14-044412-2 $ 9.95

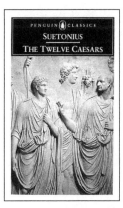

The Agricola and the Germania

Revised by S. A. Hanford
Translated and introduced by
H. Mattingly

The Agricola, Tacitus's eulogistic description of his father-in-law, the governor of Roman Britain, contains the first detailed account of the British Isles. *The Germania*, an ethnographical account of the Germanic tribes, contrasts the primitive virtues of the Germans with the degeneracy of contemporary Rome.

176 pp.   0-14-044241-3 $ 9.95

The Annals of Imperial Rome

Translated and introduced by
Michael Grant

Surviving passages from Tacitus's last and best-known work cover the reigns of Tiberius, Gaius (Caligula), Claudius, and Nero, and detail the Roman Empire at its zenith and the foundations of modern Europe.

464 pp.   0-14-044060-7 $ 9.95

The Histories

Translated and introduced by
Kenneth Wellesley

The surviving books of *The Histories* reconstruct the terrible events of the year of the Four Emperors (A.D. 69), which shook the whole edifice of the Empire.

336 pp.   0-14-044150-6 $ 9.95

The Jugurthine War and The Conspiracy of Catiline

Translated and introduced by
S. A. Hanford

These are the only surviving works by a man who held various public offices in Rome and was a friend of Caesar's and an opponent of Cicero's.

240 pp.   0-14-044132-8 $ 9.95

The Twelve Caesars

Foreword by Michael Grant
Translated and revised by Robert Graves

One of the most fascinating and colorful of all Latin histories vividly records incidents in the lives of the first twelve Caesars: Julius, Augustus, Tiberius, Gaius (Caligula), Claudius, Nero, Galba, Otho, Vitellius, Vespasian, Titus, and Domitian. 📖

320 pp.   0-14-044072-0 $ 9.95

THUCYDIDES
C. 4TH CENT. B.C., GREEK

The History of the Peloponnesian War
Revised Edition

Introduced by M. I. Finley
Translated by Rex Warner

The eight books of Thucydides' account of the clash between two great powers, Athens and Sparta, are contained in Rex Warner's acclaimed modern translation.

656 pp.   0-14-044039-9 $ 8.95

VOLTAIRE
1694–1778, FRENCH

Letters on England

Translated and introduced by Leonard Tancock

Also known as the *Lettres philosophiques*, Voltaire's response to his exile in England offered the French public of 1734 a panoramic view of English culture. Perceiving them as a veiled attack against the ancien régime, however, the French government ordered the letters burned, and Voltaire persecuted.

160 pp.   0-14-044386-X $ 8.95

REBECCA WEST
1892–1983, ENGLISH

Black Lamb and Grey Falcon
A Journey through Yugoslavia

A magnificent blend of cultural commentary, travel journal, and historical insight, this volume—written on the eve of World War II—probes the troubled history of the Balkans and their uneasy alliance of ethnic groups. Diana Trilling called *Black Lamb and Grey Falcon* "one of the great books of our century."

20TH-CENTURY CLASSICS

1,200 pp.   0-14-018847-9 $ 20.00

XENOPHON
C. 431 B.C.–C. 352 B.C., GREEK

A History of My Times

Introduced with notes by George Cawkwell
Translated by Rex Warner

Continuing the story of the Peloponnesian War where Thucydides left off, Xenophon records the politics and battles that brought about the ultimate decline of Greece.

432 pp.   0-14-044175-1 $ 9.95

The Persian Expedition

Introduced by George Cawkwell
Translated by Rex Warner

Xenophon's account of his march with the Ten Thousand against the barbarian Persians forms one of the great adventure stories in history.

376 pp.   0-14-044007-0 $ 9.95

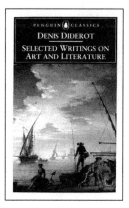

Classical Literary Criticism

Translated and introduced by
T. S. Dorsch

This collection presents three classical discussions of creative writing—Aristotle's *Poetics*, Horace's *Ars Poetica*, and the treatise *On the Sublime*, falsely attributed to Dionysius Longinus.

160 pp.   0-14-044155-7 $ 8.95

MATTHEW ARNOLD
1822–1888, ENGLISH

Selected Prose

Edited and introduced by J. P. Keating

Substantial extracts from *On Translating Homer, Essays in Criticism, Culture and Anarchy*, and *Friendship's Garland*, as well as prefaces, essays, and letters on literary criticism, education, and other topics convey the multidimensional Arnold.

480 pp.   0-14-043058-X $ 10.95

CHARLES BAUDELAIRE
1821–1867, FRENCH

Selected Writings on Art and Literature

Translated and introduced by
P. E. Charret

This collection of criticism by one of the most discerning observers of the nineteenth century also reveals the elegance of expression of one of the greatest poets of France.

464 pp.   0-14-044606-0 $ 12.95

MALCOLM COWLEY
1898–1989, AMERICAN

Exile's Return
A Literary Odyssey of the 1920s

Introduced by Donald W. Faulkner

Malcolm Cowley's intimate portrait of America's "Lost Generation" provides the defining account of the 1920s literary exodus of Fitzgerald, Hemingway, Crane, Dos Passos, Cowley, and many others to Europe.

20TH-CENTURY CLASSICS
352 pp.   0-14-018776-6 $ 12.95

DENIS DIDEROT
1713–1784, FRENCH

Selected Writings on Art and Literature

Translated and introduced by
Geoffrey Bremner

In this collection Diderot, the great master of the Enlightenment, explores reality and representation in art, literature, and theatre in a series of direct, entertaining opinions and dialogues.

432 pp.   0-14-044588-9 $ 12.95

Fantasia of the Unconscious and Psychoanalysis and the Unconscious

These two pioneering essays, written in response to Freud's work with the unconscious, are Lawrence's brilliant attempts to redefine the unconscious as "only another word for life."

20TH-CENTURY CLASSICS

256 pp.   0-14-018199-7 $ 9.95

Studies in Classic American Literature

Lawrence expounds on Franklin's *Autobiography*, Cooper's Leatherstocking novels, Poe's tales, *The Scarlet Letter*, *Moby-Dick*, *Leaves of Grass*, and other works.

20TH-CENTURY CLASSICS

190 pp.   0-14-018377-9 $ 9.95

JOHN RUSKIN
1819–1900, ENGLISH

Selected Writings

Edited by Kenneth Clark

Writings on art, literature, politics, nature, and his own characters convey the range of Ruskin's intellect and the tenor of his era.

384 pp.   0-14-043355-4 $ 13.99

Unto This Last and Other Stories

Edited and introduced with notes by Clive Wilmer

The complete text of *Unto This Last*, Ruskin's influential critique of the science of political economy and the doctrine of unhindered industrialization, is presented with selections from *Modern Painters*, *The Stones of Venice*, and *Fors Clavigera*.

368 pp.   0-14-043211-6 $ 9.95

LITERATURE

Beowulf

Translated and introduced by Michael Alexander

This heroic Old English poem, perhaps the most significant work to survive from the Anglo-Saxon period, is rendered in an eloquent verse translation.

176 pp.   0-14-044268-5 $ 5.95

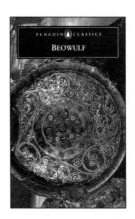

Beowulf

Edited and introduced with glossary and notes by Michael Alexander

This edition is not a literary translation; rather, the Anglo-Saxon verse text on the left-hand page is faced by a page on which almost every word is glossed. In addition, succinct footnotes clarify historical and cultural matters.

272 pp.   0-14-0433377-5 $ 10.95

Beowulf

Translated and introduced by David Wright

Based on Norse legend, this prose translation of the epic depicts the Scandinavian warrior and his struggles against monsters.

128 pp.   0-14-044070-4 $ 5.95

Book of Dede Korkut

Edited by Lewis Geoffrey

Twelve stories set in the heroic age of the Oghuz Turks combine elements of nomadic society with later Islamic culture, bringing to life an untamed civilization and its unforgettable characters.

256 pp.   0-14-044298-7 $ 8.95

A Book of English Essays

Edited by W. E. Williams

Sixty-four of the greatest English essays by twenty-five writers from Bacon and Addison to Huxley and Pritchett.

384 pp.   0-14-043153-5 $ 6.95

The Death of King Arthur

Translated and introduced by James Cable

Set in the twilight of the Arthurian world, this medieval romance tells of Lancelot's adultery with Guinevere, the arrival of the treacherous Mordred, and the deaths of both Arthur and Lancelot.

240 pp.   0-14-044255-3 $ 9.95

Early American Writing

For a description, see HISTORY AND POLITICS.

Four Stories by American Women

Edited and introduced by Cynthia Griffin Wolff

Representing four American women writers who flourished in the period following the Civil War, this prominent collection contains "Life in the Iron Mills," Rebecca Harding Davis; "The Yellow Wallpaper," Charlotte Perkins Gilman; "The Country of the Pointed Firs," Sarah Orne Jewett; and "Souls Belated," Edith Wharton.

240 pp.   0-14-039076-6 $ 8.95

The Greek Alexander Romance

Translated and introduced by Richard Stoneman

One of the most influential works of late classical Greek literature, this fast-paced, wonderfully exuberant entertainment portrays Alexander's fabulous adventures.

208 pp.   0-14-044560-9 $ 10.95

Greek Literature
An Anthology

Edited by Michael Grant

The whole range of Greek poetry and prose is highlighted, from Homer and Hesiod to the Hellenistic poets and the work of Ptolemy, Galen, and Plotinus.

496 pp.   0-14-044323-1 $ 10.95

King Arthur's Death

Translated and introduced by Brian Stone

Modern verse translations of two Midlands Arthurian epics provide a vivid contrast of medieval poetic tone and narrative style: the alliterative *Morte Arthure* (Northeast Midlands, c. 1400) and the stanzaic *Le Morte Arthur* (Northwest Midlands, c. 1350).

320 pp.   0-14-044445-9 $ 9.95

The Nibelungenlied

Translated by A. T. Hatto

This great German epic poem, written during the fourteenth century, is the principal literary source of Richard Wagner's *The Ring*.

416 pp.   0-14-044137-9 $ 9.95

The Owl and the Nightingale/ Cleanness/St. Erkenwald

Translated and introduced by Brian Stone

Three poems in verse translation exemplify the three major genres of medieval religious writing—saint's legend, Bible epic, and religious debate.

272 pp.   0-14-044245-6 $ 6.95

The Quest of the Holy Grail

Translated by P. M. Matarasso

Combining Celtic myth and Arthurian romance, this classic tale of chivalrous adventures was intended as an allegory of man's perilous search for the grace of God.

304 pp.   0-14-044220-0 $ 9.95

Sir Gawain and the Green Knight

Translated and introduced by Brian Stone

This masterpiece of medieval alliterative poetry by an unknown fourteenth-century author is both magical and human, full of drama and descriptive beauty.

176 pp.   0-14-044092-5 $ 6.95

The Song of Roland

Translated and introduced with notes by Glyn S. Burgess

Chronicling the massacre in A.D. 778 of Charlemagne's army at Roncesvalles, this age-old French epic transforms a legendary defeat into an allegorical clash between Christianity and paganism.

224 pp.   0-14-044532-3 $ 7.95

Tales from the Thousand and One Nights

Translated by N. J. Dawood

This volume includes the finest and best known of the *Tales*, representing an expression of the secular imagination in revolt against the religious austerity of other works of medieval Near Eastern literature.

416 pp.   0-14-044289-8 $ 9.95

Three Gothic Novels

Edited by Peter Fairclough
Introduced by Mario Praz

Horace Walpole's *The Castle of Otranto*, published in 1765, is the prototype of all Gothic novels; William Beckford's *Vathek* combines Gothic romanticism with Oriental exoticism; Mary Shelley's *Frankenstein* is a masterpiece of Gothic horror.

512 pp.   0-14-043036-9 $ 8.95

ADOMNÁN OF IONA
C. 625–704, IRISH

Life of St. Columba

For a description, see RELIGION.

AESOP
C. 6TH CENT. B.C, GREEK

Fables of Aesop

Translated by S. A. Hanford

Whether Aesop was a Greek slave of the sixth century B.C. or merely a name tacked onto a tradition, and whether morality, expediency, or plain entertainment was the intention, these 207 tales ensure their own survival.

234 pp.   0-14-044043-7 $ 7.95

Le Grande Meaulnes

Translated by Frank Davison

The only novel by a young man killed in action in World War I, this is a masterly exploration of the transition from boyhood to manhood.

20TH-CENTURY CLASSICS

206 pp.   0-14-018282-9 $ 7.95

La Regenta

Translated and introduced by John Rutherford

An outstanding work of nineteenth-century Spanish literature, this novel set in a provincial town explores an intelligent woman's unsuccessful quest for fulfillment through marriage, adultery, and religion.

736 pp.   0-14-044346-0 $ 12.95

Little Women

Introduced by Elaine Showalter

Alcott's portrait of the March girls— Meg, Jo, Beth, and Amy— is a classic American feminist novel, reflecting the tension between cultural obligation and artistic and personal freedom.

608 pp.   0-14-039069-3 $ 6.95

Work
A Story of Experience

Introduced by Joy S. Kasson

Work is a story about a nineteenth-century-woman's search for a meaningful life through work outside the family sphere. It is at once Alcott's exploration of her own personal conflicts as well as a social critique of America.

320 pp.   0-14-039091-X $ 10.95

LOUISA MAY ALCOTT
1832–1888, American

In Jo March, the feisty heroine of the ever popular *Little Women* (1869), Louisa May Alcott created not only an enduring favorite for readers from the 1870s to the present, but a personification of herself. She was one of four daughters of Bronson Alcott, a Transcendentalist and friend to Thoreau and Emerson. Alcott, like Jo, held positions as a governess, a teacher, and a "lady's companion," while turning out Gothic thrillers and other works of popular fiction; in *Work* she described her sometimes menial methods of supporting herself. In addition to *Little Women,* Alcott wrote several well-known novels about the March family and its descendants. Active in the feminist movement, Alcott was the first woman to register in Concord when, in 1879, Massachusetts granted women limited suffrage.

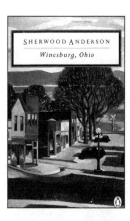

SHERWOOD ANDERSON
Winesburg, Ohio

HORATIO ALGER, JR.
1832–1899, AMERICAN

Ragged Dick and Struggling Upward

Introduced by Carl Bode

Alger's characteristic theme of youths achieving the American dream through hard work, resistance to temptation, and goodwill is presented in these two tales which reflect nineteenth-century life.

304 pp.   0-14-039033-2 $ 9.95

KINGSLEY AMIS
B. 1922, ENGLISH

Lucky Jim

Introduced by David Lodge

Lucky Jim—the hilarious story of Jim Dixon's adjustment to the protocol of teaching in the stuffy bourgeois world of the university—originally published in 1954, was the first British novel to plumb the comic possibilities of modern academic life.

20TH-CENTURY CLASSICS
254 pp.   0-14-018630-1 $ 9.95

MULK RAJ ANAND
B. 1905, INDIAN

Coolie

This poetic novel—by one of the most highly regarded Indian novelists writing in English—portrays the picaresque adventures of Munoo, a young boy forced to leave his village and make his way in the world.

20TH-CENTURY CLASSICS
288 pp.   0-14-018680-8 $ 10.95

Untouchable

Preface by E. M. Forster

Anand, hailed as his country's Charles Dickens, presents a portrait of India's untouchables written with an urgency and fury that has made this his most controversial and richest novel.

20TH-CENTURY CLASSICS
160 pp.   0-14-018395-7 $ 7.95

SHERWOOD ANDERSON
1876–1941, AMERICAN

Winesburg, Ohio

Introduced by Malcolm Cowley

Sherwood Anderson's 1919 volume of interconnected stories about an ordinary small town whose citizens struggle with extraordinary dreams and grotesque disappointments—*Winesburg, Ohio* has become an emblematic saga of American loneliness.

20TH-CENTURY CLASSICS
256 pp.   0-14-018655-7 $ 6.95

APOLLONIUS
C. 3RD CENT. B.C., GREEK

The Voyage of the Argo
Translated and introduced by E. V. Rieu

Apollonius used the manner and matter of epics but wrote from a personal viewpoint, as a critical observer, in his *Argonautica*, the only full remaining account of Jason's voyage in quest of the Golden Fleece.

224 pp.   0-14-044085-2 $ 8.95

LUDOVICO ARIOSTO
1474–1533, ITALIAN

Orlando Furioso
Translated by Barbara Reynolds

With a dazzling kaleidoscope of adventures, ogres, monsters, barbaric splendour, and romance, this epic poem stands as one of the greatest works of the Italian Renaissance.

Part I: 832 pp.   0-14-044311-8 $ 12.95
Part II: 800 pp.   0-14-044310-X $ 14.95

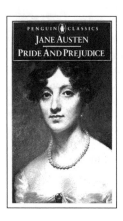

MATTHEW ARNOLD
1822–1888, ENGLISH

Selected Poems
For a description, see POETRY.

Selected Prose
For a description, see LITERARY CRITICISM.

JANE AUSTEN
1775–1817, ENGLISH

Emma
Edited by Ronald Blythe

One of Austen's most captivating heroines despite her faults, Emma Woodhouse progresses from the mismanagement of other people's affairs to a resolution of her own in this comedy of self-deceit and self-discovery.

480 pp.   0-14-043010-5 $ 4.95

Lady Susan, The Watsons, Sanditon
Edited by Margaret Drabble

These three works—one novel unpublished in her lifetime and two unfinished fragments—reveal Jane Austen's development as a great artist.

224 pp.   0-14-043102-0 $ 5.95

Mansfield Park
Edited by Tony Tanner

Conceived on a larger scale than Austen's earlier works, *Mansfield Park* is a profound and witty look at the tensions within a family and the changes that occur when guests disrupt the family's ordinary patterns.

464 pp.   0-14-043016-4 $ 5.95

Northanger Abbey

Edited by Anne Henry Ehrenpreis

This light and amusing parody reflects Austen's distaste for the absurdities of "Gothic" novels and their impossibly perfect heroines and unlikely events.

256 pp.   0-14-043074-1 $ 4.95

Persuasion

Edited by D. W. Harding

Like her earlier works, Austen's last novel is a tale of love and marriage; here, however, the heroine is more mature and the tone more somber.

400 pp.   0-14-043005-9 $ 4.95

Pride and Prejudice

Edited by Tony Tanner

A wonderful social comedy, with unerring dialogue, satisfying love stories, and an enchanting heroine, this novel embodies Austen's belief that the truly civilized maintain a balance between energy and reason. 🖵

400 pp.   0-14-043072-5 $ 4.95

Sense and Sensibility

Edited by Tony Tanner

In this, the first of her major novels, Austen depicts with subtle precision two strikingly different sisters and their search for husbands, power, and social position.

374 pp.   0-14-043047-4 $ 4.95

JANE AUSTEN and
CHARLOTTE BRONTË
1775–1817, ENGLISH
1816–1855, ENGLISH

The Juvenilia of Jane Austen and Charlotte Brontë

Edited by Frances Beer

This collection provides the opportunity to discover the first examples of Austen's neoclassical elegance and Brontë's mastery of the romantic spirit.

400 pp.   0-14-043267-1 $ 7.95

ISAAC BABEL
1894–1941, RUSSIAN

Collected Stories

Edited and introduced by David McDuff

These stories, including Babel's masterpiece, *Red Cavalry,* illuminate the author's lifelong struggle both to remain faithful to his Russian-Jewish roots and yet to be free of them, a duality of vision which infuses his work with a powerful energy.

20TH-CENTURY CLASSICS
400 pp.   0-14-018462-7 $ 11.95

HONORÉ DE BALZAC
1799–1850, FRENCH

The Black Sheep

Translated by Donald Adamson

Two brothers, one a dashing, handsome ex-soldier, the other a sensitive artist, struggle to recover the family inheritance in a novel that explores the devastation that poverty can bring.

344 pp.   0-14-044237-5 $ 9.95

César Birotteau

Translated and introduced by Robin Buss

In this powerful novel about business, the petite bourgeoisie, and human failure—set in 1819, at the dawn of the new age of capitalism—Balzac pioneered a new genre: the tragedy of the little man.

320 pp.   0-14-044641-9 $ 9.95

The Chouans

Translated by Marion Ayton Crawford

The first volume in Balzac's lifework, comprehensively entitled *The Human Comedy*, this tale of Royalist uprising against the post-revolutionary republic is rendered with characteristic passion and mastery of detail.

392 pp.   0-14-044260-X $ 9.95

Cousin Bette

Translated by Marion Ayton Crawford

Vividly bringing to life the rift between the old world and the new, *Cousin Bette* is an incisive study of vengeance, and the culmination of Balzac's *The Human Comedy*.

448 pp.   0-14-044160-3 $ 8.95

Cousin Pons

Translated by Herbert J. Hunt

The companion novel to *Cousin Bette*, *Cousin Pons* offers a diametrically opposite view of the nature of family relationships, focusing on a mild, harmless old man.

336 pp.   0-14-044205-7 $ 9.95

Eugénie Grandet

Translated by Marion Ayton Crawford

The love of money and the passionate pursuit of it, a major theme in *The Human Comedy*, is brilliantly depicted in the story of Grandet and his obsession with amassing gold and achieving power.

256 pp.   0-14-044050-X $ 8.95

A Harlot High and Low

Translated by Rayner Heppenstall

Finance, fashionable society, and the intrigues of the underworld and of the police system form the heart of this powerful novel, which introduces the satanic genius Vautrin, one of the greatest villains in world literature.

558 pp.   0-14-044232-4 $ 9.95

History of the Thirteen

Translated by Herbert J. Hunt

This trilogy of stories, purporting to be the history of a secret society, laid the foundation for Balzac's *Scenes of Parisian Life* and is a stunning evocation of all ranks of society.

392 pp.   0-14-044301-0 $ 9.95

Lost Illusion

Translated by Herbert J. Hunt

This novel of a young man who is bored with provincial life and who tries to make his way in Parisian society is part of Balzac's *The Human Comedy*.

384 pp.   0-14-044251-0 $ 10.95

A Murky Business

Translated by Herbert J. Hunt

Set earlier than most of Balzac's *The Human Comedy*, this unflinching look at the relationship between political power and morality includes Napoleon, Talleyrand, and Fouché as characters.

224 pp.   0-14-044271-5 $ 9.95

Old Goriot

Translated by Marion Ayton Crawford

The intersecting lives of a group of people living in a working-class boarding-house in nineteenth-century Paris form the background of this indictment of the cruelty of city society.

304 pp.   0-14-044017-8 $ 7.95

Selected Short Stories

Translated by Sylvia Raphael

This collection includes "El Verdugo," "Domestic Peace," "A Study in Feminine Psychology," "An Incident in the Reign of Terror," "The Conscript," "The Red Inn," "The Purse," "La Grande Bretèche," "A Tragedy by the Sea," "The Atheist's Mass," "Facino Cane," and "Pierre Grassou."

272 pp.   0-14-044325-8 $ 8.95

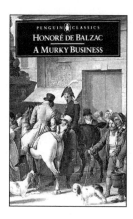

Ursule Mirouet

Translated by Donald Adamson

An essentially simple tale about the struggle and triumph of innocence, this novel also reveals Balzac's lifelong fascination with the occult.

272 pp.   0-14-044316-9 $ 8.95

The Wild Ass's Skin

Translated by Herbert J. Hunt

Balzac is concerned with the choice between ruthless self-gratification and asceticism, dissipation and restraint, in a novel powerful in its symbolism and its realistic depiction of decadence.

288 pp.   0-14-044330-4 $ 9.95

WILLIAM BECKFORD
1760–1844, ENGLISH

Vathek and Other Stories
Edited and introduced by Malcolm Jack

This collection of writings features the complete text of Beckford's best known book, *Vathek*. Beckford's talent for satire emerges in selections from the *Biographical Memoirs*, a collection of essays on imaginary artists, and the novel *Azemia*, a scathing attack on English politics. His travel diaries reveal a man of great perceptiveness and intelligence who found the lure of the unconventional irresistible.

352 pp.   0-14-043350-1 $ 9.95

APHRA BEHN
D. 1689, ENGLISH

Oroonoko, The Rover and Other Works
Edited and introduced by Janet Todd

This rich collection of works by Aphra Behn—poet, playwright, novelist, feminist, activist, and spy—reveals the talents of the first professional woman writer in English.

400 pp.   0-14-043338-4 $ 8.95

EDWARD BELLAMY
1850–1898, AMERICAN

Looking Backward
2000–1887
Edited and introduced by Cecelia Tichi

When first published in 1888, *Looking Backward* initiated a national political- and social-reform movement. This profoundly utopian tale addresses the anguish and hope of its age, as well as having lasting value as an American cultural landmark.

240 pp.   0-14-039018-9 $ 8.95

SAUL BELLOW
B. 1915, AMERICAN

The Dangling Man

Published in 1947, Saul Bellow's first novel was hailed by Edmund Wilson in the *New Yorker* as "one of the most honest pieces of testimony of a whole generation who have grown up during the Depression and war."

20TH-CENTURY CLASSICS

208 pp.   0-14-018935-1 $ 10.95

SAUL BELLOW
B. 1915, American

Saul Bellow was born in Canada of Jewish immigrant parents and reared and educated in Chicago. A winner of numerous prizes including the Pulitzer Prize (1975), the Nobel Prize for Literature (1976), and three National Book Awards, Bellow often delineates the experiences of the conflicted Jewish-American intellectual who struggles to deal with spiritual and humanistic dilemmas in a world that has shed its traditional values and ethics. He has been praised for his vision, his ear for detail, his humor, and the masterful artistry of his prose.

Mr. Sammler's Planet

Introduced by Stanley Crouch

As the country anticipates the first moon shot, and visions of Utopia vie with predictions of imminent apocalypse, Sammler, a Holocaust survivor, recalls the horrors of the past while enmeshed in the madness of the present, and finds himself intrigued by the possibilities of the future.

20TH-CENTURY CLASSICS
352 pp.   0-14-018936-X $ 9.95

Seize the Day

Introduced by Cynthia Ozick

Deftly interweaving humor and pathos, Bellow evokes in the climactic events of one day the full drama of one man's search to affirm his own worth and humanity.

20TH-CENTURY CLASSICS
144 pp.   0-14-018937-8 $ 9.95

The Victim

The Victim is the story of a man who finds himself succumbing to the story of a stranger who accuses him of ruining his life. Unable to shake the man loose or stop his own self-doubts and suspicions, Leventhal descends into a nightmare of paranoia and fear.

20TH-CENTURY CLASSICS
288 pp.   0-14-018938-6 $ 11.95

PENGUIN CLASSICS
APHRA BEHN
OROONOKO, THE ROVER AND OTHER WORKS

ARNOLD BENNETT
1867–1931, ENGLISH

Anna of the Five Towns

Introduced by Frank Swinnerton

Rife with Bennett's characteristic details—village prayer meetings, dark interiors, rent collection—this brilliant work of social observation describes the destructive power of evangelism and industrial expansion at work in a small moralistic community.

20TH-CENTURY CLASSICS
240 pp.   0-14-018015-X $ 9.95

The Card

Bennett used the life of a fellow townsman as the basis for this entertaining novel, a hilarious story of a rogue whose every bad deed turns to gold.

20TH-CENTURY CLASSICS
224 pp.   0-14-018017-6 $ 7.95

Clayhanger

Edited and introduced by
Andrew Lincoln

The first part of Bennett's famous trilogy set in the Five Towns, this story of a young man's growth from adolescence to middle age reveals Bennett's fascination with both the romance and the ugliness of the manufacturing industry.

20TH-CENTURY CLASSICS

628 pp.   0-14-018269-1 $ 9.95

The Grand Babylon Hotel

Introduced by Frank Swinnerton

Focusing on Theodore Racksole's discovery of the world inside the luxury hotel he purchased on a whim, Bennett's novel records the mysterious comings and goings of the eccentric aristocrats and conspirators who grace the corridors.

20TH-CENTURY CLASSICS

224 pp.   0-14-018019-2 $ 8.95

The Old Wives' Tale

First published in 1908, this perceptive novel of English provincial life details the affairs of two suffering sisters, while mirroring the achievements of the French realists.

20TH-CENTURY CLASSICS

624 pp.   0-14-018255-1 $ 9.95

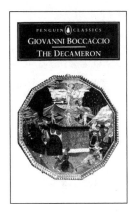

BÉROUL
c. 12TH CENT.

The Romance of Tristan

Translated by Alan S. Fredrick

This edition contains perhaps the earliest and most elemental version of the tragic legend in a distinguished prose translation. Alan S. Fredrick summarizes missing episodes and includes a translation of "The Tale of Tristan's Madness."

176 pp.   0-14-044230-8 $ 8.95

GIOVANNI BOCCACCIO
1313–1375, ITALIAN

The Decameron

Translated by G. H. McWilliam

Read as a social document of medieval times, as an earthy counterpart to Dante's *Divine Comedy*, or even as an early manifestation of the dawning spirit of the Renaissance, *The Decameron* is a masterpiece of imaginative narrative whose background is the Florentine plague of 1348.

840 pp.   0-14-044269-3 $ 10.95

HEINRICH BÖLL
1917–1985, GERMAN

Billiards at Half-past Nine

This is the story of an opponent of fascism called into battle to command retreating German forces of the Second World War. At war's end, he struggles to return to a normal life, structured by a daily regime of billiards. His rigorous routine, and the control he seeks over his memories, is upset by the return of a powerful political friend.

20TH-CENTURY CLASSICS
288 pp.   0-14-018724-3 $ 10.95

Children Are Civilians Too
Translated by Leila Vennewitz

These twenty-six short stories are stunning portraits of ordinary people in the dark post-war years in Germany and sharply illustrate Böll's finely nuanced storytelling at its best.

20TH-CENTURY CLASSICS
208 pp.   0-14-018725-1 $ 10.95

The Clown
Translated by Leila Vennewitz

Böll's story is of Hans Schneir, an artist in despair, but a sensitive observer of other people's lives, in the years during and after Hitler's rise to power.

20TH-CENTURY CLASSICS
272 pp.   0-14-018726-X $ 10.95

HEINRICH BÖLL
1917–1985, German

In a country eager to forget its Nazi past, Heinrich Böll struggled to come to terms not only with the war years but with the collective amnesia that enveloped German society, politics, and literature in the years that followed. Böll was an early member of the famous "Gruppe 47," an informal association formed in 1947 by German writers anxious to play a part in shaping their country's future. Böll had served in the infantry during World War II, and his early stories are stark reflections on the futility and insanity of war. In his later novels, Böll turned his attention to the moral vacuum at the heart of the "new" Germany and the smug complacency of the new bourgeoisie born of the "economic miracle" of the 1950s. Combining a poetic eye and sharp sense of social satire, Böll lay bare society's hypocrisies in works that explored the lives of people marginalized by society because of their beliefs, economic status, or non-conformist behavior. His support of left-wing causes in the 1960s and 1970s incurred vicious attack by the right-wing press. Thrust into a position of moral leadership, Böll is considered by many to be the conscience of post-war Germany. In 1972, he was awarded the Nobel Prize in Literature, the first German to be so honored since Thomas Mann in 1929; he remained a towering figure in European literature until his death in 1985.

Group Portrait with Lady

Translated by Leila Vennewitz

In this dazzling satirical novel, Böll weaves together the absurd but all too human stories of an array of characters, who all knew Leni Pfeiffer—a German woman whose secret romance with a Soviet prisoner of war both sustains and threatens her life.

20TH-CENTURY CLASSICS
416 pp.   0-14-018727-8 $ 11.95

The Lost Honor of Katherina Blum

Translated by Leila Vennewitz

In this masterful journey through a labyrinth of threats, untruths, and violence, a young woman's association with a hunted man makes her the target of an unscrupulous journalist, and she sees only one way out.

20TH-CENTURY CLASSICS
160 pp.   0-14-018728-6 $ 9.95

TADEUSZ BOROWSKI
1922–1951, POLISH

This Way for the Gas, Ladies and Gentlemen

Introduced by Jan Kott
Translated by Barbara Vedder

Published in Poland after World War II, this collection of concentration camp stories stands as cruel testimony to the level of inhumanity of which man is capable.

20TH-CENTURY CLASSICS
192 pp.   0-14-018624-7 $ 9.95

ELIZABETH BOWEN
1899–1973, IRISH

Death of the Heart

The story of adolescent love in London during the 1930s, this novel reflects not only Bowen's sense of comedy but her insight into human motivations.

20TH-CENTURY CLASSICS
320 pp.   0-14-018300-0 $ 9.95

Eva Trout

This complex portrait of a beautiful and unsettling eccentric's personal journey across Europe and America displays Bowen's keen psychological insight and descriptive talents.

20TH-CENTURY CLASSICS
272 pp.   0-14-018298-5 $ 10.95

The Heat of the Day

In this evocation of London during the Blitz, Bowen describes the intimacies—and the betrayals—that develop in a society freed from the usual rules and conventions.

20TH-CENTURY CLASSICS
336 pp.   0-14-018301-9 $ 9.95

The House in Paris

Introduced by A. S. Byatt

Bowen's subtle novel tells a disturbing, delicate story about four people in a house in Paris, united by tragedy—two children waiting, and upstairs a young woman tending her dying mother.

20TH-CENTURY CLASSICS
240 pp.   0-14-018303-5 $ 10.95

Last September

A sharply perceived comedy of manners set in the time of the Irish Troubles, this novel also bears a foreshadowing of the tragedies to come.

20TH-CENTURY CLASSICS

208 pp.   0-14-018304-3 $ 9.95

The Little Girls

A sixty-year-old woman places a classified ad to find two grade school companions, setting off a chain of events that conjures up the revelations inherent in summoning up childhood.

20TH-CENTURY CLASSICS

240 pp.   0-14-018305-1 $ 9.95

ANNE BRONTË
1820–1849, ENGLISH

Agnes Grey

*Edited and introduced by
Angeline Goreau*

A young governess experiences disillusionment and discovers love in this elegant novel, which George Moore found "the most perfect prose narrative in English literature."

272 pp.   0-14-043210-8 $ 5.95

The Tenant of Wildfell Hall

Edited by G. D. Hargreaves

Set in the rakish Regency society and written during the 1840s, when the oppression of women was at its height, this novel is striking in its bold treatment of the issue of women's equality.

512 pp.   0-14-043137-3 $ 6.95

CHARLOTTE BRONTË
1816–1855, ENGLISH

Jane Eyre

Edited by Q. D. Leavis

The strange and unforgettable romance between Jane Eyre and Rochester is at heart the frankly told story of a spirited and intelligent woman who refuses to accept her appointed place in society.

496 pp.   0-14-043011-3 $ 4.95

The Professor

Edited and introduced by Heather Glen

Published posthumously in 1857, Brontë's first novel is a thinly disguised account of her love for M. Heger.

320 pp.   0-14-043311-2 $ 5.95

Shirley

Edited by Andrew and Judith Hook

Brontë grapples with the social and political issues of the mid-nineteenth century in a sweeping novel that explores the possibilities of reconciling romantic love and the demands of social convention.

624 pp.   0-14-043095-4 $ 6.95

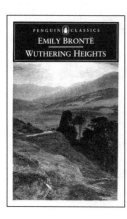

Villette

Edited by Mark Lilly

An autobiographical novel, *Villette* is a moving portrait of the tensions between inner and outer experience and of the anguish of unrequited love. 🖾
624 pp.   0-14-043118-7 $ 7.95

EMILY BRONTË
1818–1848, ENGLISH

Wuthering Heights

Edited by David Daiches

Emily Brontë's only novel, the story of love between Catherine Earnshaw and the wild Heathcliff is a dark, brooding, and passionate masterpiece. 🖾
382 pp.   0-14-043001-6 $ 4.95

CHARLES BROCKDEN BROWN
1771–1810, AMERICAN

Edgar Huntly
Or, Memoirs of a Sleep-Walker

Edited and introduced by Norman S. Grabo

One of the first American Gothic novels, Brown's finest work, set in Philadelphia in 1787, mirrors the social and political temperaments of post-revolutionary America.
288 pp.   0-14-039062-6 $ 10.95

Wieland and
Memoirs of Carwin the Biloquist

Edited and introduced by Jay Fliegelman

A terrifying account of the fallibility of the human mind and, by extension, of democracy itself, *Wieland* (1798) brilliantly reflects the psychological, social, and political concerns of the early American republic. In the fragmentary sequel *Memoirs*, Brown explores Carwin's bizarre previous history: as a manipulated disciple of the charismatic utopian Ludloe.
416 pp.   0-14-039079-0 $ 10.95

THE BRONTËS

"Life rarely offers us the gift of three talents, all major in some degree, all of one blood, and of the same generation, using not only the same form, the novel, but using it in a way that makes the fullest possible use of personal experience. Moreover the experience is not only that of events, people and society encountered together, but also a private spiritual and imaginative life lived for the most formative years in common." —**Wendy A. Craik**

GEORGE DOUGLAS BROWN
1869–1902, SCOTTISH

The House with the Green Shutters
Edited by Dorothy Porter

In this chronicle of a tyrannical father and his passive, bullied family, Brown subverted the sentimental view of Scottish pastoral life put forth by his contemporaries.

20TH-CENTURY CLASSICS

272 pp.   0-14-018278-0 $ 9.95

IVAN BUNIN
1870–1953, RUSSIAN

The Gentleman from San Francisco and Other Stories
Translated and introduced by
David Richards and Sophie Lund

This collection of stories hails from one of Russia's great realist writers, a modern heir to Chekhov and Turgenev and winner of the Nobel Prize.

20TH-CENTURY CLASSICS

224 pp.   0-14-018552-6 $ 9.95

JOHN BUNYAN
1628–1688, ENGLISH

The Pilgrim's Progress
Edited by Roger Sharrock

Written in prison, John Bunyan's chronicle of Christian's pilgrimage to the Celestial City is a powerful allegory of the conflict between religion and society.

384 pp.   0-14-043004-0 $ 6.95

FRANCES BURNEY
1752–1840, ENGLISH

Evelina
Edited and introduced by
Margaret Anne Doody

This portrait of female independence and the intrigues of the social classes introduced an entirely new form of novel—the comedy of manners—when it was published anonymously in 1778.

544 pp.   0-14-043347-3 $ 9.95

EDGAR RICE BURROUGHS
1875–1950, AMERICAN

Tarzan of the Apes
Introduced by John Seelye

This 1914 novel gave birth to one of the most legendary characters in fiction, an ideal image of pure animalistic power at odds with the civilzed world.

20TH-CENTURY CLASSICS

320 pp.   0-14-018464-3 $ 8.95

SAMUEL BUTLER
1612–1680, ENGLISH

Erewhon
Edited by Peter Mudford

Butler's tale of a traveler to a remote island, based on his experiences in New Zealand, combines the elements of traditional utopian fiction and the picaresque novel; the influence of The Origin of Species on Butler's writing is apparent.

272 pp.   0-14-043057-1 $ 9.95

The Way of All Flesh

*Edited by Richard Hogart and
James Cochrane*

With wit, irony, and, sometimes, rancor,
Butler savages the smug values and beliefs of a Victorian family.

446 pp.   0-14-043012-1 $ 8.95

GEORGE WASHINGTON CABLE
1844–1925, AMERICAN

The Grandissimes

Introduced by Michael Kreyling

Setting forth formidable arguments for
racial equality, Cable's novel of feuding
Creole families in early nineteenth-
century New Orleans blends post–Civil
War social dissent and Romanticism.

384 pp.   0-14-043322-8 $ 10.95

ABRAHAM CAHAN
1860–1951, LITHUANIAN

The Rise of David Levinsky

*Edited and introduced by
Jules Chametzky*

Originally published in 1917, this classic
of Jewish-American literature tells the
story of a young immigrant who works
his way to success in the garment industry, but is at a loss in matters of love and
identity.

20TH-CENTURY CLASSICS
544 pp.   0-14-018687-5 $ 11.95

LUIS VAZ DE CAMOËNS
c. 1525–1580, PORTUGUESE

The Lusiads

*Translated and introduced by
William C. Atkinson*

Employing *The Aeneid* as a model and
invoking the whole divine order of
Olympus, *The Lusiads*—the national
epic of Portugal—recounts the ten-
month voyage by which Vasco da Gama
opened the seaway to India.

256 pp.   0-14-044026-7 $ 8.95

CAO XUEQIN
c. 1715–1763, CHINESE

Story of the Stone (in five volumes)
Volume 1: The Golden Days (Chapters 1–26)

Translated by David Hawkes

"Indisputably the greatest masterpiece
... of all the Chinese novels" (*The New
York Review of Books*), this novel of
manners, also known as *The Dream of
the Red Chamber,* is now complete in
five volumes.

544 pp.   0-14-044293-6 $ 11.95

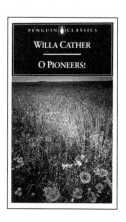

Volume 2: The Crab-Flower Club (Chapters 27–53)

Translated by David Hawkes

606 pp.   0-14-044326-6 $ 11.95

Volume 3: The Warning Voice (Chapters 54–80)

Translated by David Hawkes

640 pp.   0-14-044370-3 $ 11.95

Volume 4: The Debt of Tears (Chapters 81–98)

Edited by E. Gao
Translated by John Minford

400 pp.   0-14-044371-1 $ 10.95

Volume 5: The Dreamer Awakes (Chapters 99–120)

Edited by E. Gao
Translated by John Minford

384 pp.   0-14-044372-X $ 11.95

BALDESAR CASTIGLIONE
1478–1529, ITALIAN

The Book of the Courtier

Translated by George Bull

In a series of imagined conversations, Castiglione creates deeply felt and historically accurate accounts of the Italian Renaissance at the height of its splendor.

368 pp.   0-14-044192-1 $ 9.95

WILLA CATHER
1873–1947, AMERICAN

My Ántonia

Introduced by John J. Murphy

Cather's portrait of a remembered American girlhood on the Nebraskan prairie at the end of the nineteenth century alternates between insightful lyricism and naturalistic description, as she explores the rich relationship of Ántonia and the narrator, Jim Burden.

20TH-CENTURY CLASSICS

304 pp.   0-14-018764-2 $ 8.95

O Pioneers!

Introduced by Blanche Gelfant

The first of Cather's renowned prairie novels, *O Pioneers!* established new territory and a new voice in American literature—turning the story of ordinary Midwesterners and immigrants into authentic literary characters.

20TH-CENTURY CLASSICS

224 pp.   0-14-018775-8 $ 6.95

CAO XUEQIN
c. 1715–1763, Chinese

Divided into five volumes, *The Story of the Stone* charts the glory and decline of the illustrious Jia family (a story which closely accords with the fortunes of Cao Xueqin's own family). The characters are set against a rich tapestry of humor, realistic details, and delicate poetry which accurately reflects the ritualized hurly-burly of Chinese family life. But over and above the novel hangs the constant reminder that there is another plane of existence—a theme which affirms the Buddhist belief in a supernatural scheme of things.

The Blazing World and Other Writings

Edited and introduced by Kate Lilley

These remarkable works of the flamboyant Margaret Cavendish, the seventeenth-century Duchess of Newcastle, reveal not only a radical feminist, but a transgressor of every literary and sexual role and code. The title piece is the first work of science fiction ever written, depicting a utopia ruled by a warrior queen.

272 pp.   0-14-043372-4 $ 10.95

Don Quixote

Translated and introduced by J. M. Cohen

The adventures of Cervantes's idealistic knight errant and his simple but astute squire, Sancho Panza, is not only a hilarious parody of the romances of chivalry but an exploration of the relationship between the real and the illusionary.

944 pp.   0-14-044010-0 $ 7.95

MIGUEL DE CERVANTES
1547–1616, Spanish

Miguel de Cervantes was born in Alcalá de Henares, Spain, in 1547. As a young man serving in the Spanish wars against the Ottoman Empire, he was captured by the Barbary pirates and sent into slavery in Algeria in 1575. After many attempts at escape, he was finally ransomed in 1580, an act which reduced his family to poverty. Returning to Madrid, Cervantes entered public service (including a stint commandeering supplies for the Spanish Armada) and was so ill-suited to the job that he was jailed for gross irregularities in his accounts. Although his first novel, *La Galatea*, was written in 1585, and he wrote poetry and drama (only two of his thirty plays survive), it was not until the publication of *Don Quixote* in 1605 that Cervantes gained fame as a writer. An immediate success in his native country, the novel soon became a favorite abroad. The intricate, multi-layered structure of the novel, and Cervantes's brilliant exploration of the relationship between art and life, had tremendous impact on the development of the modern novel; the works of writers from Fielding and Smollett to Twain, Dostoyevsky, and even Kafka, all bear traces of the influence of Cervantes' masterpiece.

Exemplary Stories

Translated and introduced by C. A. Jones

Included in this collection are "The Little Gypsy Girl," "Rinconete and Cortadillo," "The Glass Graduate," "The Deceitful Marriage," and "The Dog's Colloquy."

256 pp.   0-14-044248-0 $ 8.95

GEOFFREY CHAUCER
c. 1342–1400, ENGLISH

The Canterbury Tales

Translated by Nevill Coghill

This edition captures the entire body of Chaucer's masterpiece in a thoroughly readable modern translation that preserves much of the freshness and racy vitality of the original text.

528 pp.   0-14-044022-4 $ 4.95

Love Visions

Translated and introduced by Brian Stone

Spanning Chaucer's working life, these four poems move from the conventional allegorical "love visions" toward realistic storytelling and provide a marvelous self-portrait. This selection includes "The Book of the Duchess," "The House of Fame," "The Parliament of the Birds," and "The Legend of Good Women."

272 pp.   0-14-044408-4 $ 8.95

Troilus and Criseyde

Translated by Nevill Coghill

Chaucer's depiction of passionate sexual love, his grasp of tragedy, and his sense of the ridiculous hidden in the sublime are all displayed in this poetic retelling of the classical story set during the Trojan War.

336 pp.   0-14-044239-1 $ 8.95

MEDIEVAL LITERATURE

In medieval Western Europe there was a glorious flowering of literature, mostly in versified story. National heroes like Arthur, Roland, and Charlemagne, together with their knights—such romantic characters as Gawain, Lancelot, and Oliver—live and love, fight and die, in tales of deeds of love and derring-do, often undertaken for passionate, enigmatic women such as Guinevere, Isolde, and Criseyde.

In the powerful religious literature, emergent Christianity battles bloodily against pagans and monsters, and vigorous saintliness is expressed in Bible epic, devotional lyric, and poetic sermon. William Langland *(Piers the Ploughman)* criticizes society from a practical missionary standpoint, and Chaucer celebrates worldly life, including courtly love and knockabout sex, in humane and often funny poetry.

Many of these stories and themes survive vividly in our culture, in new novels and poems, as well as in film, and musical and visual art; but here are the great medieval works themselves, in accessible modern translation.

The Duel and Other Stories

*Translated and introduced by
Ronald Wilks*

Chekhov's mastery of the short story is illuminated in these examples: "Murderer," "The Wife," "The Black Monk," "Terror," and "Big Volodyu and Small Volodyu."

240 pp.   0-14-044415-7 $ 8.95

Fiancée and Other Stories

*Translated and introduced by
Ronald Wilks*

Although Chekhov is also famed as a dramatist, he actually studied medicine in Moscow and launched his literary career through humorous contributions to journals. The stories in this selection support evidence of his prolific creativity: "On Official Business," "Rothschild's Fiddle," "Pleasant Women," "Three Years," "With Friends," "The Bet," "New Villa," "At a Country House," "Beauties," "His Wife," and "The Student."

240 pp.   0-14-044470-X $ 5.95

The Kiss and Other Stories

*Translated and introduced by
Ronald Wilks*

As Chekhov's confidence developed, his reputation grew along with his expertise. The trilogy "The Man in a Case," "Gooseberries," and "Concerning Love" are examples pf this period. This collection also includes "A Case History," "In the Gully," and "Anna, Round the Neck."

224 pp.   0-14-044336-3 $ 5.95

Lady with Lapdog and Other Stories

Translated by David Magarshack

After the 1892 famine, Chekhov moved to a small estate not far from Moscow where he continued his pursuit of realistically characterizing Russian society. "Ward 6," one of the stories in this volume, was written there. Included also are "Grief," "Agafya," "Misfortune," "A Boring Story," "The Grasshopper," "Ariande," "The House with an Attic," "Ionych," and "The Darling."

288 pp.   0-14-044143-3 $ 7.95

The Party and Other Stories

*Translated and introduced by
Ronald Wilks*

In addition to "The Party," this volume includes "A Woman's Kingdom," "My Life: A Provincial's Story," "An Unpleasant Business," and "A Nervous Breakdown."

240 pp.   0-14-044452-1 $ 4.95

Plays

For a description, see DRAMA.

CHARLES W. CHESNUTT
1858–1932, AMERICAN

The House Behind the Cedars
Edited and introduced by Donald Gibson

An early masterwork among American literary treatments of miscegenation, Chesnutt's story is of two young African-Americans who decide to pass for white in order to claim their share of the American dream.

20TH-CENTURY CLASSICS

304 pp.　0-14-018685-9　$ 10.95

The Marrow of Tradition
Edited and introduced by Eric J. Sundquist

This novel is based on a historically accurate account of the Wilmington, North Carolina, "race riot" of 1898, and is a passionate portrait of the betrayal of black culture in America, by an acclaimed African-American writer.

20TH-CENTURY CLASSICS

336 pp.　0-14-018686-7　$ 12.95

G. K. CHESTERTON
1874–1936, ENGLISH

The Club of Queer Trades

Sleuth Basil Grant, Chesterton's literary hero and alter ego, stars in six fascinating crime stories in which no crime has been committed.

20TH-CENTURY CLASSICS

128 pp.　0-14-018387-6　$ 7.95

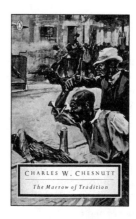

The Man Who Was Thursday
Introduced by Kingsley Amis

Named after the days of the week for security reasons, the seven members of the Central Anarchist Culture vow to destroy the world. "It remains the most thrilling book I have ever read." — Kingsley Amis

20TH-CENTURY CLASSICS

192 pp.　0-14-018388-4　$ 6.95

The Napoleon of Notting Hill

G. K. Chesterton's first novel, originally published in 1904, portrays the transformation of the outrageous, portly, and outspoken Auberon King into His Majesty the King—a distinctly unroyal royal determined to fight for the rights of the individual.

20TH-CENTURY CLASSICS

160 pp.　0-14-018389-2　$ 8.95

The Awakening and Selected Stories

Edited and introduced by Sandra M. Gilbert

First published in 1889, *The Awakening* caused such discomfort and outrage for its brutal honesty that it was figuratively banned until the 1960s, when it was recognized as a forthright pioneering feminist novel. Other selections include "Emancipation," "At the 'Cadian Ball," and "Désirée's Baby."

320 pp.   0-14-039022-7 $ 5.95

A Vocation and a Voice

Stories

Edited and introduced by Emily Toth

Published for the first time as the author intended, this is a collection of avant-garde stories by the author of the controversial novel *The Awakening*.

192 pp.   0-14-039078-2 $ 7.95

Arthurian Romances

Translated by Carleton W. Carroll
Translated and introduced by William W. Kibler

Fantastic adventures abound in these courtly romances: *Erec and Enide*, *Cligés*, *The Knight of the Cart*, *The Knight with the Lion*, and *The Story of the Grail*.

528 pp.   0-14-044521-8 $ 9.95

KATE CHOPIN

1851–1904, American

Like most women of her time, Kate Chopin (1851–1904) was modest about both her goals and her accomplishments. Her writings, however, set her apart from the other members of her sex: influenced by European writers—particularly de Maupassant—she wrote with a subtlety and sensuality that was rare in nineteenth-century American literature. While her early local-color stories set in Louisiana enjoyed great popularity, her explorations of the difficulties women faced in society—as well as her revelations about their emotional and sexual longings—were considered far too graphic for most American magazines. Chopin's private life, like her writing, was unconventional, if not "shocking." Her circle included outspoken reformers, argumentative writers, and avant-garde artists; her male admirers were often married men, and her female friends often the center of local scandals. She renounced organized religion and probably experimented with altered states of consciousness. Rediscovered by critics in the 1960s, she is regarded today as a pioneering voice in feminist literature.

HUGO CLAUS
B. 1929, DANISH

The Sorrow of Belgium
Translated by Arnold J. Pomerans

In this prizewinning, majestic story of a boy's coming of age in Nazi-occupied Belgium, ten-year-old Louis's own growth toward maturity—amidst social and political upheaval, the horrors of war, and especially his parents' own collaboration with the occupiers—mirrors that of his country.

20TH-CENTURY CLASSICS

608 pp.   0-14-018801-0 $ 11.95

JOHN CLELAND
1709–1789, ENGLISH

Fanny Hill
Or Memoirs of a Woman of Pleasure
Edited and introduced by Peter Wagner

This infamous story of a prostitute's rise to respectability holds a place in the history of the English novel alongside the work of Richardson, Fielding, and Smollett.

240 pp.   0-14-043249-3 $ 7.95

WILLIAM COBBETT
1763–1835, ENGLISH

Rural Rides
Edited and introduced by George Woodcock

The emergence of industrialism in nineteenth-century England is the subject of William Cobbett's journals.

542 pp.   0-14-043023-7 $ 6.95

COLETTE
1873–1954, FRENCH

Chance Acquaintances and Julie de Carneilhan

In *Chance Acquaintances*, Colette describes her sojourn at a health resort where she befriends the handsome Gerard Haume and his invalid wife. *Julie de Carneilhan*, the last full-length novel Colette wrote, offers insights into her feelings about her own second marriage.

20TH-CENTURY CLASSICS

128 pp.   0-14-010032-6 $ 7.95

Chéri and The Last of Chéri

Introduced by Raymond Mortimer

Earthy, sensuous, and daring, this classic portrait of the ill-fated affair between a very young man and a middle-aged woman is a wonderful introduction to Colette's extravagant imaginative imagery—and her profound understanding of the human heart.

20TH-CENTURY CLASSICS

256 pp.   0-14-018317-5 $ 9.95

The Claudine Novels

These four novels—*Claudine at School, Claudine in Paris, Claudine Married,* and *Claudine and Annie*—constitute Colette's first series of books. Written between 1900 and 1907, they chronicle the experiences of a young girl growing to maturity and display a lyricism and candor that mark the author's later works.

20TH-CENTURY CLASSICS

560 pp.   0-14-018322-1 $ 9.95

Gigi and The Cat

Master schemers are at the heart of these two short works, in which Colette demonstrates that she is wise to the ways both of Parisian women and of the animal kingdom.

20TH-CENTURY CLASSICS

160 pp.   0-14-018319-1 $ 9.95

The Ripening Seed

In *The Ripening Seed,* Colette captures that precious, painful moment when childhood innocence gives way to the birth of knowledge and desire.

20TH-CENTURY CLASSICS

128 pp.   0-14-018321-3 $ 7.95

The Vagabond

Introduced by Raymond Mortimer

In this tender and poetic tale of unrequited love and loneliness, Colette reflects on the essential fragility of human emotions.

20TH-CENTURY CLASSICS

192 pp.   0-14-018325-6 $ 9.95

WILKIE COLLINS
1824–1889, ENGLISH

Armadale

Edited and introduced by John Sutherland

This intricately plotted Victorian melodrama draws on the substance and style of the popular press of the day: fraud, bigamy, drug addiction, and domestic poisonings all rear their ugly heads as Collins chronicles the evil ways of a spectacularly beautiful but unscrupulous woman.

752 pp.   0-14-043411-9 $ 10.95

The Moonstone

Edited by J. I. M. Stewart

In this, the first modern English detective story, Collins displays an intuitive grasp of how to create the suspense and atmosphere that are the hallmarks of great mystery storytelling. 🔊

654 pp.   0-14-043014-8 $ 5.95

No Name

A tale of courage and confrontation in the world of rigid Victorian society, Collins's novel creates a vivid and disturbing view of the hypocrisy inherent in the upper class.

640 pp.   0-14-043397-X $ 11.95

The Woman in White

Edited by Julian Symons

This thriller, revolving around the identities of two mysterious women, caused great excitement when it was published in 1860 and continues to enthrall and surprise readers. 🔊

654 pp.   0-14-043096-2 $ 6.95

IVY COMPTON-BURNETT
1884–1969, ENGLISH

The Present and the Past

Cassius Clare's former wife re-enters his life nine years after their divorce, befriends his current wife, and causes a dramatic upheaval that erupts in a shocking conclusion.

20TH-CENTURY CLASSICS

176 pp.   0-14-018326-4 $ 6.95

JOSEPH CONRAD
1857–1924, ENGLISH

Almayer's Folly

Set in Malaya, Conrad's first novel charts the decline of a Dutch merchant after twenty-five years of hard struggle against overwhelming odds.

20TH-CENTURY CLASSICS

128 pp.   0-14-018030-3 $ 8.95

Chance

In *Chance,* Conrad created one of his most complex heroines—slender, dreamy, morbidly charming Flora de Barral—and one of his most unrelenting novels of emotional isolation.

20TH-CENTURY CLASSICS

400 pp.   0-14-018654-9 $ 5.95

Heart of Darkness

Edited and introduced by Robert Hampton

A masterpiece of twentieth-century writing—and arguably the first true twentieth-century novel—*The Heart of Darkness* explores the workings of the subconscious and the grim reality of imperialism. This edition includes more than seventy pages of critical commentary together with Conrad's "The Congo Diary," the record of his own 1890 journey upon which the novel is based. 🔊

20TH-CENTURY CLASSICS

208 pp.   0-14-018652-2 $ 6.95

Lord Jim

Edited by Robert Hampson
Introduced by Cedric P. Watts

Conrad's powerful portrait of a young idealist whose one moment of weakness marks his life forever probes into the nature of innocence and experience, heroism and cowardice.

20TH-CENTURY CLASSICS

384 pp.   0-14-018092-3 $ 3.95

The Nigger of the "Narcissus"

Edited and introduced by Cedric P. Watts

In his third novel and first major work Conrad explores the themes of political and psychological subversion when the "closed society" on a ship is threatened by storm and by mutiny.

20TH-CENTURY CLASSICS

208 pp.   0-14-018094-X $ 5.95

Nostromo

Edited and introduced by
Martin-Seymour Smith

Conrad's pessimistic view of the world colors this novel depicting the brutality of Latin American politics and the tragedies that inevitably ensue.

20TH-CENTURY CLASSICS

480 pp.   0-14-018371-X $ 5.95

Outcast of the Island

Marooned on a Malayan island by his own people, Willems is about to feel the consequences of his corruption.

20TH-CENTURY CLASSICS

384 pp.   0-14-018032-X $ 8.95

The Secret Agent

Edited and introduced by
Martin Seymour-Smith

A black satire of English society, this chilling tale features amoral characters on both sides of the law—fatuous civil servants and corrupt policemen, bomb-carrying terrorists, and sleazy pornographers.

20TH-CENTURY CLASSICS

272 pp.   0-14-018096-6 $ 6.95

The Shadow-Line

Edited and introduced by
Jacques Berthoud

The Shadow-Line, a masterpiece of Conrad's final period, is the story of a young captain in crisis at sea who must wrestle with his isolation and his conscience to cross the "shadow-line" between youth and adulthood.

20TH-CENTURY CLASSICS

160 pp.   0-14-018097-4 $ 7.95

Tales of Unrest

Though English was not his native language, Conrad's legacy nevertheless exhibits his tenacious grasp of expression, and hard experience gained from years at sea. This collection includes "Karain: A Memory," "The Idiots," "An Outpost of Progress," "The Return," and "The Lagoon."

20TH-CENTURY CLASSICS

202 pp.   0-14-018036-2 $ 5.95

JOSEPH CONRAD
Lord Jim

'Twixt Land and Sea

Edited and introduced by Boris Ford

Brilliantly evoking the character of the East Indies, its land, its people, and the sea, four tales—"'Twixt Land and Sea," "A Smile of Fortune," "The Secret Sharer," and "Freya of the Seven Isles"—create worlds of adventure, romance, and tragedy.

20TH-CENTURY CLASSICS

240 pp.   0-14-018392-2 $ 7.95

Typhoon and Other Stories

Edited and introduced by Paul Kirschner

Originally published in 1903, this volume, written as Conrad bid farewell to his life as a seaman, contains "Typhoon," "Falk," "Amy Foster," and "Tomorrow."

20TH-CENTURY CLASSICS

320 pp.   0-14-018257-8 $ 4.95

Under Western Eyes

Edited and introduced by Boris Ford

Against a background of ominous suspense, Conrad portrays not so much the political as the psychological state of Russia in 1911.

20TH-CENTURY CLASSICS

352 pp.   0-14-018287-X $ 8.95

Victory

A story of rescue and violent tragedy set in the Malayan archipelago, *Victory* combines high adventure with a sensitive portrayal of three drifters.

20TH-CENTURY CLASSICS

416 pp.   0-14-018359-0 $ 6.95

Within the Tides

These four powerful stories, experimental in style, illustrate Conrad's recognition of the ethical and psychological complexities behind the "simple" idea of fidelity. This collection was first published in 1915.

20TH-CENTURY CLASSICS

192 pp.   0-14-018065-6 $ 9.95

Youth/Heart of Darkness/ The End of the Tether

Edited and introduced by John Lyon

These three novels, originally published together, form a subtle, somewhat skeptical portrait of the "ages of man." Combining the traditional elements of adventure stories with psychological insights, these works demonstrate why Conrad has been hailed as a vital link between Victorian literature and the birth of the modern novel.

20TH-CENTURY CLASSICS

384 pp.   0-14-018513-5 $ 7.95

BENJAMIN CONSTANT
1767–1830, FRENCH

Adolphe

Translated by Leonard Tancock

This chronicle of the love affair between a young man and an older woman is based on the author's own stormy affair with Madame de Staël.

128 pp.   0-14-044134-4 $ 8.95

JAMES FENIMORE COOPER
1789–1851, AMERICAN

The American Democrat

Edited and introduced by George Dekker and Larry Johnston

Cooper's impassioned examination of the theory and practice of democracy in America circa 1830 is at once a denunciation of the cant he saw pervading his country's political system and a hopeful elucidation of the system's inherent possibilities.

240 pp.   0-14-039068-5 $ 6.95

The Deerslayer

Edited and introduced by Donald Pease

In this acclaimed depiction of life during America's westward movement, part of *The Leatherstocking Tales,* Cooper describes the young manhood of Natty Bumppo, his mythical hero who remains one of the most significant characters in American literature.

384 pp.   0-14-039061-8 $ 8.95

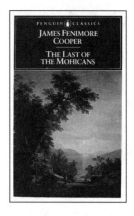

The Last of the Mohicans

Edited and introduced by Richard Slotkin

Tragic, fast-paced, and stocked with the elements of a classic Western adventure, this novel takes Natty Bumppo and his Indian friend Chingachgook through hostile Indian territory during the French and Indian War.

688 pp.   0-14-039024-3 $ 8.95

The Pathfinder

Edited and introduced by Kay Seymour House

The fourth novel in *The Leatherstocking Tales* is a "romance," the story of Natty Bumppo's unsuccessful courtship of a young woman during the French and Indian War.

496 pp.   0-14-039071-5 $ 7.95

The Pioneers

Edited and introduced by
Donald A. Ringe

The first of *The Leatherstocking Tales* introduces the mythical hero Natty Bumppo in a portrait that contrasts the natural codes of Bumppo to the rigid legal and social structures of a new settlement.

448 pp.   0-14-039007-3 $ 7.95

The Prairie

Edited and introduced by Blake Nevius

The final novel in Cooper's epic, *The Prairie,* depicts Natty Bumppo at the end of his life, still displaying his indomitable strength and dignity.

384 pp.   0-14-039026-X $ 9.95

STEPHEN CRANE
1871–1900, AMERICAN

The Red Badge of Courage and Other Stories

Edited by Pascal Covici, Jr.

Here is one of the greatest novels ever written about war and its psychological effect on the individual soldier. This edition also includes the short stories: "The Open Boat," "The Bride Comes to Yellow Sky," "The Blue Hotel," "A Poker Game," and "The Veteran."

304 pp.   0-14-039081-2 $ 7.95

RICHARD DANA
1815–1882, AMERICAN

Two Years Before the Mast
A Personal Narrative of Life at Sea

Edited and introduced by
Thomas Philbrick

Dana's realistic novel of the brutalities of maritime life also illustrates the nation's growing interest in life beyond the confines of civilization and in the reform of working-class conditions. This edition includes the author's retrospective of the voyage and the book.

576 pp.   0-14-039008-1 $ 9.95

DANTE
1265–1321, FLORENTINE

The Divine Comedy (3 volumes)
Volume 1: Inferno

Translated and introduced with notes
and commentary by Mark Musa

This vigorous new translation of *The Divine Comedy* preserves Dante's simple, natural style and captures the swift movement of the original Italian in blank verse renditions by Mark Musa. "An outstanding achievement that combines scrupulous respect for the original with an English style that is clear, unlabored, and readable." —Thomas G. Bergin, Professor Emeritus, Yale University

432 pp.   0-14-044441-6 $ 8.95

Volume 2: Purgatory

Translated and introduced with notes
and commentary by Mark Musa

400 pp.   0-14-044442-4 $ 9.95

Volume 3: Paradise

Translated and introduced with notes and commentary by Mark Musa.

450 pp.   0-14-044443-2 $ 8.95

The Divine Comedy
Volume 1: Hell

Translated by Dorothy L. Sayers

This is a revered translation that attempts to reveal Dante through his classic work as a poet of vivid personality: sublime, intellectual, humorous, simple, and tender.

352 pp.   0-14-044006-2 $ 8.95

Volume 2: Purgatory

Translated by Dorothy L. Sayers

388 pp.   0-14-044046-1 $ 8.95

Volume 3: Paradise

Translated by Dorothy L. Sayers and Barbara Reynolds

400 pp.   0-14-044105-0 $ 8.95

La Vita Nuova

For a description, see POETRY.

ALPHONSE DAUDET
1840–1897, FRENCH

Letters from My Windmill

Translated and introduced by Frederick Davies

Throughout his career, celebrated Parisian novelist Daudet remained a true son of Provence. This collection of wryly humorous stories, admired by Flaubert, Dickens, and Henry James, evokes the vital rhythms of Provençal life and Daudet's youth in the mid-nineteenth century.

224 pp.   0-14-044334-7 $ 9.95

THOMAS DE QUINCEY
1785–1859, ENGLISH

Confessions of an English Opium Eater

Edited by Alethea Hayter

De Quincey's powerful evocation of his drug-induced experience offers fascinating insight into the degeneration of a brilliant mind.

232 pp.   0-14-043061-X $ 8.95

Recollections of the Lakes and the Lake Poets

Edited and introduced by David Wright

De Quincey's observant and critical musings include a wealth of firsthand impressions, biographical minutiae, and gossip about the lives and works of Wordsworth, Southey, and Coleridge.

416 pp.   0-14-043056-3 $ 9.95

DANIEL DEFOE
1660–1731, ENGLISH

A Journal of the Plague Year

Edited by Anthony Burgess and Christopher Bristow

The shocking immediacy of Defoe's description of plague-racked London makes it one of the most convincing accounts of the Great Plague of 1665 ever written.

256 pp.   0-14-043015-6 $ 4.95

Moll Flanders

Edited and introduced by David Blewett

This tale of Moll Flanders's glorious, picaresque progress through vice, poverty, mishaps, and strange coincidences is an exuberant panorama of eighteenth-century England.

464 pp.   0-14-043313-9 $ 5.95

Robinson Crusoe

Edited by Angus Ross

Regarded as one of the first English novels, this exciting adventure story introduced one of the most enduring characters—and plots—of all time.

320 pp.   0-14-043007-5 $ 4.95

Roxana

Edited by David Blewett

Defoe's last novel, *Roxana* depicts the decline and defeat of a woman tempted by the glamour of immortality.

416 pp.   0-14-043149-7 $ 9.95

A Tour Through the Whole Island of Great Britain

Edited and abridged by Pat Rogers

Defoe endows his guide to Britain just before the Industrial Revolution with a wild inventive streak that makes this book not only a classic of travel writing but a fascinating economic and social history.

736 pp.   0-14-043066-0 $ 13.95

CHARLES DICKENS
1812–1870, ENGLISH

American Notes for General Circulation

Edited and introduced by John S. Whitley and Arnold Goldman

The youthful, still rough America of 1842 is vividly recalled in this journal of Dickens's famous tour of the country, offering a fascinating view of the New World by one of the Old World's greatest writers and social thinkers.

368 pp.   0-14-043077-6 $ 8.95

Barnaby Rudge

Edited by G. W. Spence

A superb novel of individuals caught in the horrors of the rebellion of apprentices against their masters, *Barnaby Rudge* dramatizes Dickens's fascination with private murder and public violence.

768 pp.   0-14-043090-3 $ 6.95

Bleak House

Edited by Norma Page

This sweeping panorama of English society, written late in his career, shows Dickens as a profoundly serious novelist as well as a popular entertainer.

974 pp.   0-14-043063-6 $ 8.95

The Christmas Books
Volume 1: A Christmas Carol, The Chimes

Edited by Michael Slater

Dickens's unique blend of comedy and horror and his creation of that delightful grotesque, Scrooge, continue to mark our celebrations of Christmas; *The Chimes* is a provocative satire on how the wealthy celebrate New Year's Eve. (*A Christmas Carol* 📼)

266 pp.   0-14-043068-7 $ 5.95

The Christmas Books
Volume 2: The Cricket on the Hearth, The Battle of Life, The Haunted Man

The Cricket on the Hearth is a delightful comedy set in a world of toys; *The Battle of Life* and *The Haunted Man* share the theme of the morally beneficial effects of memory.

366 pp.   0-14-043069-5 $ 6.95

David Copperfield

Edited by Trevor Blount

Written in the form of an autobiography, this is Dickens's ever-popular story of a young man growing to maturity in both affairs of the world and affairs of the heart.

960 pp.   0-14-043008-3 $ 5.95

Dombey and Son

Edited by Peter Fairclough
Introduced by Raymond Williams

Against the teeming streets of mid-Victorian London, Dickens examines Britain's new industrial power and its potential for creation and destruction.

992 pp.   0-14-043048-2 $ 6.95

Great Expectations

Edited by Angus Calder

The story of the orphan Pip and the mysterious fortune which falls into his lap is at once a sharp and grotesque comedy and a profound moral and psychological drama. 📼

512 pp.   0-14-043003-2 $ 5.95

Hard Times

Edited by David Craig

This portrait of a British mill town in the 1840s is replete with Dickensian details of life in that period. It is also a powerful attack on the then prevalent philosophy of utilitarianism, which allowed human beings to be enslaved to machines and reduced to numbers.

336 pp.   0-14-043042-3 $ 4.95

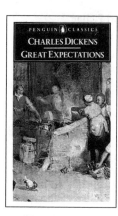

Little Dorrit

Edited by John Holloway

Dickens portrays a world of hypocrisy and sham, of exploiters and parasites, in this penetrating criticism of society, one of his last novels.

912 pp.   0-14-043025-3 $ 6.95

Martin Chuzzlewit

Edited by P. N. Furbank

Moving from sunny face to the grimmest reaches of criminal psychology, Dickens creates a classic study of selfishness and hypocrisy. 🔲

942 pp.   0-14-043574-3 $ 10.95

The Mystery of Edwin Drood

Edited by A. Cox
Introduced by Angus Wilson

Unfinished at the time of Dickens's death, this novel explores the dark opium underworld and the uneasy and violent fantasies of its inhabitants.

320 pp.   0-14-043092-X $ 5.95

Nicholas Nickleby

Edited by Michael Slater

Around his central story of Nicholas Nickleby and the misfortunes of his family, Dickens weaves a great gallery of comic types—the Crummles, Miss Petowker, the Lillyvicks—in a novel that remains a model of English comedy.

976 pp.   0-14-043113-6 $ 6.95

CHARLES DICKENS

1812–1870, English

Charles Dickens was born in Portsmouth on February 7, 1812, the second of eight children. His father, a government clerk, was imprisoned for debt and Dickens was sent to work from the age of twelve. He became a reporter of parliamentary debates for the *Morning Chronicle* and began to publish sketches in various periodicals, which were subsequently republished as *Sketches By Boz*. *The Pickwick Papers* were published in 1836–37 and became a publishing phenomenon and Dickens's characters the center of a popular cult. In his later work Dickens's social criticism became more radical and his comedy more savage. He died on June 9, 1870. Dickens's popularity during his lifetime was exceptional but, as the distinguished literary critic Walter Allen said, his influence continues to be felt and "his work has become part of the literary climate within which Western man lives."

The Old Curiosity Shop

Edited by Angus Easson

This novel contains some of Dickens's most bizarre characters, including the lecherous dwarf Quilp, as well as his most sentimental creation, the innocent Little Nell, destroyed by an evil world. 🖼

720 pp.   0-14-043075-X $ 7.95

Oliver Twist

Edited by Peter Fairclough
Introduced by Angus Wilson

In this scathing exposure of the pervasive evil of his society Dickens created three of his most memorable characters—Fagin, Bill Sykes, and the Artful Dodger. 🖼

496 pp.   0-14-043017-2 $ 5.95

Our Mutual Friend

Edited by Stephen Gill

The last novel Dickens completed before his death, this satire on wealth and its corrupting powers is darker and more complex in its symbolism than Dickens's early writing.

912 pp.   0-14-043060-1 $ 6.95

The Pickwick Papers

Edited by Robert Patten

The story of the adventures of the charming, portly Sam Weller and his Pickwick Club catapulted the twenty-four-year-old Charles Dickens to fame.

960 pp.   0-14-043078-4 $ 6.95

Selected Short Fiction

Edited by Deborah A. Thomas

Divided into three selections—"Tales of the Supernatural," "Impressionistic Sketches," and "Dramatic Monologues"—this volume reveals Dickens's recurring concerns and places them clearly in the context of related elements in his novels.

368 pp.   0-14-043103-9 $ 7.95

A Tale of Two Cities

Edited by George Woodcock

In this stirring tale of the French Revolution, Dickens reveals much about his own "psychological revolution," examining his fears and innermost conflicts through the actions of Charles Darnay, Sydney Carton, and Lucie Manette. 🖼

416 pp.   0-14-043054-7 $ 4.95

DENIS DIDEROT
1713–1784, FRENCH

Jacques the Fatalist and His Master

Introduced with notes by Martin Hall
Translated by Michael Henry

In this revolutionary novel, a leading figure of the Enlightenment celebrates the unpredictable nature of man and the world as he considers the behavior of the moral being and the philosophical dilemma of free will and determinism.

262 pp.   0-14-044472-6 $ 8.95

The Nun

Translated by Leonard Tancock

In one of the most remarkable novels of the Enlightenment, Diderot sharply criticizes conventional Christianity in a tale about a woman confined to a convent against her will.

192 pp.   0-14-044300-2 $ 7.95

Rameau's Nephew and D'Alembert's Dream

Translated by Leonard Tancock

In the form of dialogues, Diderot attacks stale conventions and offers a surprisingly modern view of life, sex, and morals.

240 pp.   0-14-044173-5 $ 9.95

BENJAMIN DISRAELI
1804–1881, ENGLISH

Coningsby,
Or The New Generation

Edited by Thom Braun

The first political novel in the English language, and Disraeli's finest work of fiction, *Coningsby* is full of wit, irreverence, intrigue, and romance—set at the time of the 1832 Reform Act, a crossroads in nineteenth-century English social history.

528 pp.   0-14-043192-6 $ 7.95

Sybil,
Or The Two Nations

Edited by Thom Braun
Introduced by R. A. Butler

So vivid is this work's exposure of the gross inequalities of Victorian society that it has become one of the most important English political novels and part of Disraeli's "Young England trilogy," along with *Coningsby* and *Tancred*.

304 pp.   0-14-043134-9 $ 7.95

JOHN DONNE
1572–1631, ENGLISH

Selected Prose

Edited and introduced by Neil Rhodes

Reflecting the metaphysical clash between poetry and religion, John Donne's works explore the relationship between self and world, capturing the conflict between the spiritual and the secular. This volume includes "Paradoxes," "Problems," "Biathanatos," "Devotions upon Emergent Occasions," letters, and sermons.

552 pp.   0-14-043239-6 $ 9.95

FYODOR DOSTOYEVSKY
1821–1881, RUSSIAN

The Brothers Karamazov
*Translated and introduced by
David McDuff*

This striking new translation of Dostoyevsky's masterful drama of parricide and family rivalry chronicles the murder of Fyodor Karamazov and the subsequent investigation and trial. This new rendition recaptures the sound, tone, and rough humor of the original. With extensive notes.

960 pp.   0-14-044527-7 $ 8.95

Crime and Punishment
*Translated and introduced by
David McDuff*

Dostoyevsky's masterpiece of modern literature is a study in the psychology of the criminal mind, an indictment of social conditions, and an engrossing portrait of Raskolnikov's Russia.

656 pp.   0-14-044528-5 $ 8.95

The Devils
Translated by David Magarshack

Denounced by radical critics as the work of a reactionary, this powerful story of Russian terrorists plotting destruction only to murder one of their own seethes with provocative political opinions.

704 pp.   0-14-044035-6 $ 7.95

The Gambler, Bobok, A Nasty Story
Translated by Jessie Coulson

Conveying all the intensity and futility of an obsession, *The Gambler* is based on Dostoyevsky's firsthand experience; "Bobok" and "A Nasty Story" are two of the author's best darkly comic stories.

240 pp.   0-14-044179-4 $ 8.95

The House of the Dead
*Translated and introduced by
David McDuff*

The four years Dostoyevsky spent in a Siberian prison inform this portrait of convicts, their diverse stories, and prison life, rendered in almost documentary detail.

368 pp.   0-14-044456-4 $ 7.95

The Idiot
Translated by David Magarshack

At the center of a novel that has the plot of a thriller, Dostoyevsky portrays the Christlike figure of Prince Mishkin, bringing readers face to face with human suffering and spiritual compassion.

672 pp.   0-14-044054-2 $ 6.95

Netochka Nezvanova

Translated and introduced by
Jane Kentish

Written as a serial, this never-completed first publication treats many of the themes that dominate Dostoyevsky's later great novels.

192 pp.   0-14-044455-6 $ 8.95

Notes from the Underground, The Double

Translated by Jessie Coulson

In *Notes from the Underground* Dostoyevsky portrays a nihilist who probes into the dark underside of man's nature; *The Double* is Dostoyevsky's classic study of a psychological breakdown.

288 pp.   0-14-044252-9 $ 7.95

Poor Folk and Other Stories

Translated and introduced by
David McDuff

Dostoyevsky's first great literary triumph, the novella *Poor Folk* is presented here, along with "The Landlady," "Mr. Prokharchin," and "Polzunkov."

288 pp.   0-14-044505-6 $ 7.95

Uncle's Dream and Other Stories

Translated and introduced by
David McDuff

Completed after five years of Siberian exile, *Uncle's Dream* is remarkable for its uncharacteristic objectivity, satire, and even farce, revealing a profound transformation in the author's worldview. This edition includes the stories "A Weak Heart," "White Nights," and "The Meek Girl."

304 pp.   0-14-044518-8 $ 9.95

RUSSIAN LITERATURE

The nineteenth-century Russian novel is perhaps unique in world literature. So great is the panoply of human existence it unfolds, so detailed and profound the analysis of human nature and psychology it offers, that the reader frequently has the sense of going beyond literature: "He who studies *Anna Karenina* studies life itself," a contemporary Russian critic is said to have remarked.

As if to confirm this universality, and to make it accessible to those who do not know Russian, succeeding generations of translators have endeavored to re-create the novels of Turgenev, Tolstoy, and Dostoyevsky in English almost since the time of their first publication in the original language. Typically, a new translation builds upon the insights gained from fresh scholarship in a field of knowledge and research that is expanding all the time.

The Penguin Classics translations of the Russian novels (and, indeed, of classical Russian literature as a whole) aim to combine a maximum of scholarly accuracy and textual faithfulness with an approach to language that is a living one, suited to the vital qualities of the originals.

The Village of Stepanchikovo

Translated and introduced by
Ignat Avsey

This work introduces a Dostoyevsky unfamiliar to most readers, revealing his unexpected talents as a humorist and a satirist. While its lighthearted tone and amusing plot make it a joy to read, it also contains the prototypes of characters who appear in his later works.

224 pp.   0-14-044658-3 $ 10.95

THEODORE DREISER
1871–1945, AMERICAN

Jennie Gerhardt

Edited and introduced by
James L. W. West III

Now restored to its complete, unexpurgated form, Dreiser's 1911 novel about a woman compromised by birth and fate contains rich critiques of American class and ethnicity as well as the foundations of literary Naturalism.

20TH-CENTURY CLASSICS

432 pp.   0-14-018710-3 $ 11.95

Sister Carrie

Introduced by Alfred Kazin

This subversive landmark novel, restored and unexpurgated, portrays the social world of turn-of-the century America through the story of a woman who survives by becoming mistress to a wealthy man.

20TH-CENTURY CLASSICS

496 pp.   0-14-018828-2 $ 10.95

GEORGE DU MAURIER
1834–1896, FRENCH

Trilby

Edited and introduced by Daniel Pick

The greatest bestseller of the nineteenth century, *Trilby* combines the sensationalism of the best commercial fiction with a fascinating look at the darkest obsessions of late nineteenth-century Europe.

336 pp.   0-14-043403-8 $ 7.95

ALEXANDER DUMAS
1802–1870, FRENCH

The Three Musketeers

Translated by Lord Sudley

Based on historic fact, *The Three Musketeers* is the stirring, romantic story of d'Artagnan, Athos, Porthos, and Aramis, and their fight to preserve the honor of their Queen.

720 pp.   0-14-044025-9 $ 8.95

MARIA EDGEWORTH
1767–1849, IRISH

Castle Rackrent and Ennui

Edited and introduced by Marilyn Butler

These are two stylish novels of Anglo-Irish relations: *Castle Rackrent* is Irish family history unreliably narrated by a loyal servant; *Ennui* is a "confession" by an aristocrat caught up in Ireland's 1798 Revolution.

368 pp.   0-14-043320-1 $ 9.95

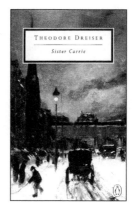

Adam Bede

Edited by Stephen Gill

The story of a beautiful country girl's seduction by a local squire and the bitter consequences is told with Eliot's peculiar, haunting power.

608 pp.   0-14-043121-7 $ 6.95

Daniel Deronda

Edited by Barbara Hardy

In this, her last novel, Eliot sought to come to terms with the society-within-a-society of English Jews, a world rarely explored by her contemporaries.

904 pp.   0-14-043020-2 $ 7.95

Felix Holt: The Radical

Edited with an introduction by Lynda Mugglestone

This edition includes appendices on the legal background of the plot and on the "Address to Working Men, by Felix Holt."

576 pp.   0-14-043435-6 $ 11.95

Middlemarch

Edited and introduced by Rosemary Ashton

This superb English novel, Eliot's finest achievement, portrays the shape and texture of a rising provincial town of the 1830s through the remarkable story of determined heroine Dorothea Brooke—an idealist and a woman of conviction trapped in an agonizing marriage to the egotistical Mr. Casaubon. 🖾

880 pp.   0-14-043388-0 $ 7.95

THEODORE DREISER
1871–1945, American

A hardworking Midwestern newspaperman, lacking much formal education and beset by bouts of depression, Dreiser had a series of turbulent love affairs and marriages. He was forced to struggle to have his controversial first novel, *Sister Carrie* (1900), published, although it had been enthusiastically received by Frank Norris, then a publisher's assistant. In *Sister Carrie* and in *Jennie Gerhardt* (1911), Dreiser presented a powerful and disturbing view of the repressive moral and social conventions of America. Dreiser's well-known novel *An American Tragedy* (1925), in which he again indicts America's materialistic values, was based on the Chester Gilette-Grace Brown murder case of 1906.

The Mill on the Floss

Edited by Antonia Byatt

This affectionate and perceptive portrayal of childhood and adolescence in rural England features an imaginative heroine whose spirit closely resembles Eliot's own.

696 pp.   0-14-043120-9 $ 6.95

Romola

Edited by Andrew Sanders

Eliot re-creates the upheavals of fifteenth-century Florence, including the expulsion of the Medici and the rise of Savonarola, in a work that is central to her career as a novelist.

736 pp.   0-14-043139-X $ 6.95

Scenes of Clerical Life

Edited by David Lodge

Published at a time when religious issues were hotly debated, this collection of stories reflects Eliot's search for a religion of humanity that preserves the best in traditional Christianity.

432 pp.   0-14-043087-3 $ 5.95

Selected Essays, Poems, and Other Writings

Edited by A. S. Byatt and N. D. Warren Introduced by A. S. Byatt

Rich in a wit and energy dissimilar from that of her novels, this collection of Eliot's shorter works includes contributions to the *Westminster Review*, selections from *Impressions of Theophrastus Such*, passages from her translations of Feuerbach and Strauss, the "Notes on Form in Art," and other major essays.

544 pp.   0-14-043148-9 $ 11.95

Silas Marner

Edited by Q. D. Leavis

Against the background of the Industrial Revolution, Eliot draws a genial, mellow portrait of a village community threatened by the changes to come. 📖

272 pp.   0-14-043030-X $ 4.95

WILLEM ELSSCHOT
1882–1960, DUTCH

Villa des Roses

Translated and introduced by Paul Vincent

The guests of a first-class boardinghouse are embroiled in seductions and suicide in this black comedy of manners by the acclaimed novelist of the Netherlands.

20TH-CENTURY CLASSICS

160 pp.   0-14-018427-9 $ 8.95

OLAUDAH EQUIANO
1745–1797, NIGERIAN

The Interesting Narrative and Other Writings

Edited and introduced by Vincent Carretta

This account of the slave trade by a native African, former slave, and loyal British subject is a spirited autobiography, a tale of spiritual quest and fulfillment, and a sophisticated treatise on religion, politics, and economics.

368 pp.   0-14-0433485-2 $ 9.95

ERASMUS
c. 1466–1536, DUTCH

Praise of Folly

For a description, see HISTORY AND POLITICS.

WOLFRAM VON ESCHENBACH
C. 1170–C. 1220, GERMAN

Parzival

Translated and introduced by A. T. Hatto

This prose translation of von Eschen-bach's thirteenth-century narrative poem re-creates and completes the story of the Holy Grail left unfinished by Chrétien de Troyes.

448 pp.   0-14-044361-4 $ 9.95

Willehalm

Translated and introduced by Marion E. Gibbs and Sidney M. Johnson

A martial epic and a tragic romance, this is the story of the consequences of Willehalm's elopement with Giburc, written by the greatest narrative poet of the German Middle Ages.

1,320 pp.   0-14-044399-1 $ 9.95

RICHARD FARIÑA
D. 1966, AMERICAN

Been Down So Long It Looks Like Up to Me

Introduced by Thomas Pynchon

In this classic novel of the 1960s—an unerring, corrosively comic depiction of a campus in revolt—Fariña evokes the period as precisely, wittily, and poignantly as F. Scott Fitzgerald captured the Jazz Age.

20TH-CENTURY CLASSICS

352 pp.   0-14-018930-0 $ 11.95

HENRY FIELDING
1707–1754, ENGLISH

Amelia

Edited and introduced by David Blewett

A story of domestic and social disen-chantment, Fielding's last novel repre-sents a move away from the comic style of his earlier works toward a more subtle analysis of contemporary society's ills.

608 pp.   0-14-043229-9 $ 7.95

HENRY FIELDING

1707–1754, English

Henry Fielding was born at Sharpham Park in Somerset in 1707. In London, between 1729 and 1739, he wrote some twenty-five dramatic pieces including a series of topical satires which lampooned Sir Robert Walpole and his government. In reaction to these plays, Walpole introduced the Stage Licensing Act in 1737, which effectively ended Fielding's career as a dramatist. His novel writing career began with *Shamela* in 1741, a burlesque written in reaction to what he saw as the smug morality propounded by Richardson's *Pamela*. He then published his own alternative conception of the art and purpose of the novel, *Joseph Andrews*, which achieved immediate popularity. His masterpiece *Tom Jones*, one of the great comic novels in English literature, was published in 1749. Commissioned as a justice of the peace for Westminster, Fielding devoted the last years of his life to the field of criminal justice.

Jonathan Wild

Edited and introduced by David Nokes

This edition includes Fielding's satiric novel—based on the life of a notorious eighteenth-century thief—and Daniel Defoe's account of the real-life Jonathan Wild.

280 pp.   0-14-043151-9 $ 8.95

Joseph Andrews

Edited by R. F. Brissenden

One of the richest, sanest, and funniest satires ever written, this story of a young man's determination to save his virtue features Parson Adams, one of the first great comic characters in English fiction.

344 pp.   0-14-043114-4 $ 5.95

Tom Jones

Edited by R. P. C. Mutter

A novel rich in incident and coincidence, this picaresque tale of a young man mocks the literary—and moral—conventions of Fielding's time.

912 pp.   0-14-043009-1 $ 5.95

RONALD FIRBANK
1886–1926, ENGLISH

Valmouth and Other Novels

Three short novels of gleeful debauchery, effete sensibility, and extravagant character by the colorful early-twentieth-century writer Firbank.

20TH-CENTURY CLASSICS

256 pp.   0-14-018055-9 $ 9.95

GUSTAVE FLAUBERT
1821–1880, FRENCH

Bouvard and Pécuchet

Translated by A. J. Krailsheimer

Unfinished at the time of Flaubert's death in 1880, *Bouvard and Pécuchet* features two Chaplinesque figures in a farce that mocks bourgeois stupidity and the banality of intellectual life in France.

336 pp.   0-14-044320-7 $ 6.95

Madame Bovary

Translated and introduced by Geoffrey Wall

A new translation of Flaubert's landmark story unfolds the desperate love affair of Emma Bovary, the bored provincial housewife who abandons her husband in defiance of bourgeois values. 🖭

320 pp.   0-14-044526-9 $ 7.95

Salammbô

Translated by A. J. Krailsheimer

An epic story of lust, cruelty, and sensuality, this historical novel is set in Carthage in the days following the First Punic War with Rome.

288 pp.   0-14-044328-2 $ 9.95

Sentimental Education

Translated by Robert Baldick

Flaubert skillfully re-creates the fiber of his times and society in this novel of a young man's romantic attachment to an older woman.

432 pp.   0-14-044141-7 $ 5.95

The Temptation of St. Antony

Translated and introduced by Kitty Mrosovsky

One of Flaubert's earliest works, this prose poem is a series of visions and arguments quite different in mood and style from his other writings.

304 pp.   0-14-044410-6 $ 7.95

Three Tales

Translated by Walter J. Cobb

In *A Simple Life* Flaubert recounts the life of a pious servant girl; *The Legend of St. Julian, Hospitaller* gives insight into medieval mysticism; and *Hérodias* is a powerful story of the martyrdom of St. John the Baptist.

128 pp.   0-14-044106-9 $ 6.95

THEODOR FONTANE
1819–1898, GERMAN

Effi Briest

Translated by Douglas Parmée

This story of a woman's adultery and its consequences is a stunning portrait of the rigidity of the Prussian aristocracy in the mid-nineteenth century.

272 pp.   0-14-044190-5 $ 8.95

FORD MADOX FORD
1873–1939, ENGLISH

The Good Soldier

Ford explores the deceptions of Edward Ashburnham, an impeccable English gentleman and soldier with an overbearing ruthlessness in affairs of the heart.

20TH-CENTURY CLASSICS

240 pp.   0-14-018081-8 $ 7.95

ANATOLE FRANCE
1844–1924, FRENCH

The Gods Will Have Blood

Translated and introduced by Frederick Davies

Set during the French Revolution in the fifteen months preceding the fall of Robespierre, this novel by Nobel Prize–winner Anatole France powerfully re-creates the Terror—a period of intense and virtually indiscriminate violence.

20TH-CENTURY CLASSICS

256 pp.   0-14-018457-0 $ 9.95

HAROLD FREDERIC
1856–1898, AMERICAN

The Damnation of Theron Ware

Introduced by Scott Donaldson

A candid inquiry into the intertwining of religious and sexual fervor, and a telling portrait of America at the end of the nineteenth century, this novel foreshadows the rise of Naturalism in American literature.

512 pp.   0-14-039025-1 $ 9.95

WILLIAM GADDIS
B. 1922, AMERICAN

JR
Introduced by Frederick Karl

Winner of the National Book Award in 1976, the hero of this novel of epic comedy and satire is an eleven-year-old capitalist who parlays Navy surplus forks and some defaulted bonds into a vast empire of free enterprise.

20TH-CENTURY CLASSICS

752 pp.   0-14-018707-3 $ 13.95

The Recognitions
Introduced by William Gass

First published in 1955 and considered one of the most profound works of fiction of this century, *The Recognitions* tells the story of a painter-counterfeiter who forges out of love, not larceny, in an age where fakes have become indistinguishable from the real.

20TH-CENTURY CLASSICS

976 pp.   0-14-018708-1 $ 14.95

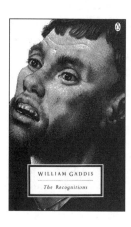

HAMLIN GARLAND
1860–1940, AMERICAN

A Son of the Middle Border

For a description, see AUTOBIOGRAPHY AND BIOGRAPHY.

ELIZABETH GASKELL
1810–1865, ENGLISH

Cranford and Cousin Phillis
Edited by P. J. Keating

Both *Cranford,* an affectionately ironic and understated depiction of an early Victorian country town, and *Cousin Phillis,* the story of an unfulfilled love affair, are concerned with the transition from old values to new.

368 pp.   0-14-043104-7 $ 6.95

Mary Barton
Edited by Stephen Gill

In this novel set in provincial England, Gaskell offers not only a love story and a murder, but an incisive exposition of the dangers inherent in the lack of communication between the classes.

488 pp.   0-14-043053-9 $ 6.95

North and South
Edited by R. Colin

The industrial unrest and misery of mid-nineteenth-century Manchester, England, are depicted in this novel about relationships between the employed and their employers.

544 pp.   0-14-043055-5 $ 6.95

Wives and Daughters
Edited by Frank Glover-Smith

This story of a marriage and its effect on many people is a work of wit, intelligence, and perception comparable to the best of Jane Austen and George Eliot.

720 pp.   0-14-043046-6 $ 9.95

GEORGE GISSING
1857–1903, ENGLISH

New Grub Street
Edited by Bernard Bergonzi

Through Edwin Reardon, a struggling novelist, and his friends on Grub Street, Milvain, a journalist, and Yule, an embittered critic, Gissing brings to life the literary climate of 1880s' London.

560 pp.   0-14-043032-6 $ 10.95

The Odd Women
Introduced by Elaine Showalter

A refreshing antidote to Victorian novels celebrating romantic love and marriage, *The Odd Women* is a dramatic look at the actual circumstances, options, and desires of women, told with psychological and political realities which are astonishingly contemporary.

416 pp   0-14-043379-1 $ 8.95

ELLEN GLASGOW
1873–1945, AMERICAN

Virginia
Introduced by Linda Wagner-Martin

Published in 1913, suffragist Ellen Glasgow's daring and ironic novel of a disillusioned wife and mother explores the issues of gender, race, and religion in the patriarchal society of the American South.

432 pp.   0-14-039072-3 $ 4.95

WILLIAM GODWIN
1756–1836, ENGLISH

Caleb Williams
Things as They Are, or The Adventures
Edited and introduced by Maurice Hindle

A psychological detective novel about power, Caleb Williams was an imaginative contribution to the radical cause in the English debate on the French Revolution.

448 pp.   0-14-043256-6 $ 9.95

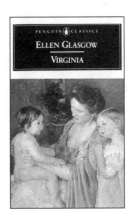

JOHANN W. VON GOETHE
1749–1832, GERMAN

Elective Affinities

Translated and introduced by
R. J. Hollingdale

Condemned as immoral when it was first published, this novel reflects the conflict Goethe felt between his respect for the conventions of marriage and the possibility of spontaneous passion.

304 pp.   0-14-044242-1 $ 10.95

Faust, Parts 1 and 2

For a description, see DRAMA.

Italian Journey

For a description, see TRAVEL.

Selected Verse

For a description, see POETRY.

Sorrows of Young Werther

Translated and introduced by
Michael Hulse

Based partly on Goethe's unrequited love for Charlotte Buff, this novel of pathological sensibility strikes a powerful blow against Enlightenment rationalism.

144 pp.   0-14-044503-X $ 8.95

NIKOLAI GOGOL
1809–1852, RUSSIAN

Dead Souls

Translated by David Magarshack

The hero of this satiric masterpiece is Gogol's most beguiling and devilish creation, a man who buys dead serfs; Gogol's attempts to continue the story in two more books obsessed him, eventually driving him to madness and death.

384 pp.   0-14-044113-1 $ 9.95

Diary of a Madman and Other Stories

Translated by Ronald Wilks

These five stories, including "Diary of a Madman," "The Overcoat," and "The Nose," are a delightful introduction to Gogol's peculiar and strikingly original imagination.

192 pp.   0-14-044273-1 $ 6.95

OLIVER GOLDSMITH
1730–1774, BRITISH

The Vicar of Wakefield

Edited and introduced by Stephen Coote

This charming comedy is an artful send-up of the literary conventions of Goldsmith's time—the pastoral scene, the artificial romance, the stoic bravery of the hero—culminating in a highly improbable denouement.

224 pp.   0-14-043159-4 $ 5.95

IVAN GONCHAROV
1812–1891, RUSSIAN

Oblomov

Translated by David Magarshack

Goncharov's detached yet sympathetic portrait of the humdrum life of his ineffectual and slothful hero is a tragicomedy that introduced one of literature's most universal and familiar figures.

496 pp.   0-14-044040-2 $ 9.95

EDMUND GOSSE
1849–1928, ENGLISH

Father and Son

Edited and introduced by Peter Abbs

An account of the religious fanaticism surrounding his upbringing, Gosse's novel also serves as a brilliant and moving document of Victorian social and intellectual history.

20TH-CENTURY CLASSICS

224 pp.   0-14-018276-4 $ 8.95

ROBERT GRAVES
1895–1985, ENGLISH

Collected Short Stories

These are superb, lyrical stories by one of the most versatile writers in the English language—poet, novelist, critic, mythographer, translator, and autobiograper Robert Graves.

20TH-CENTURY CLASSICS

304 pp.   0-14-018484-8 $ 11.95

JOHANN W. VON GOETHE
1749–1832, German

Goethe was born in Frankfurt-am-Main in 1749 and studied at Leipzig, where he showed interest in the occult, and in Strassburg, where Herder introduced him to Shakespeare's works and folk poetry. He produced some essays and lyrical verse, and at twenty-four wrote *Goetz von Berlichingen*, a play which brought him national fame and established him in the current Sturm und Drang movement. *Sorrows of Young Werther*, a tragic romance, was an even greater success. Goethe began work on *Faust* before being invited to join the government at Weimar. His interest in the classical world led him to leave suddenly for Italy in 1768, and *The Italian Journey* recounts his travels there. Returning to Weimar, he started the second part of *Faust*, encouraged by Schiller, and during this late period wrote many other works, including *Elective Affinities*. He also directed the State Theater and worked on scientific theories in evolutionary botany, anatomy, and color.

HENRY GREEN
1905–1973, ENGLISH

Loving—Living—Party Going

Introduced by John Updike

Each one of these three startling, original novels by England's enigmatic author Henry Green deals with class differences and the challenges of love.

20TH-CENTURY CLASSICS

528 pp.   0-14-018691-3 $ 14.95

Nothing—Doting—Blindness

This volume introduces the first and final novels of the vastly imaginative Henry Green, once described by W. H. Auden as "the finest English novelist."

20TH-CENTURY CLASSICS

512 pp.   0-14-018692-1 $ 14.95

Pack My Bag

For a description, see AUTOBIOGRAPHY and BIOGRAPHY.

GRAHAM GREENE
1904–1991, ENGLISH

Brighton Rock

Greene's chilling exposé of violence and gang warfare in the pre-war English underworld features a protagonist who is the embodiment of evil.

20TH-CENTURY CLASSICS

256 pp.   0-14-018492-9 $ 9.95

A Burnt-Out Case

A world-famous architect who has lost interest in his life and art anonymously begins work at a leper colony in order to cure his "disease of the mind."

20TH-CENTURY CLASSICS

200 pp.   0-14-018539-9 $ 9.95

The Comedians

Three men meet on a ship bound for Haiti, a world in the grip of the corrupt "Papa Doc" and his sinister secret police, the Tontons Macoute.

20TH-CENTURY CLASSICS

288 pp.   0-14-018494-5 $ 9.95

HENRY GREEN
1905–1973, English

Born in 1905 to an upper-class family, Henry Green was educated at Eton and Oxford. He wrote his first novel, *Blindness* (1926), while still at Oxford. Although he worked full-time in his family's engineering business—beginning as an apprentice on the shop floor in 1927 and eventually becoming managing director—Green diligently pursued his writing career, producing nine novels, a memoir, and many short stories, non-fiction pieces, and reviews. A writer of extraordinary originality, Green has been applauded by many leading literary figures. His novels were called "as solid and glittering as gems," by Anthony Burgess; Eudora Welty declared "Green's remains the most interesting and vital imagination in English fiction in our time"; and John Updike, who acknowledges his own debt to Green, wrote "Green's novels are sufficiently unlike any others, sufficiently assured in their perilous, luminous fullness, to warrant the epithet 'incomparable.'"

GRAHAM GREENE
The End of the Affair

The Confidential Agent

This is a psychological thriller about a man sent from the Continent to England to buy coal at almost any price. His adventures have high stakes: not only the fate of a continental government in the midst of civil war, but also his own destiny—a man who is trusted by no man, and is capable of trusting nobody.

20TH-CENTURY CLASSICS

208 pp.   0-14-018538-0 $ 7.95

The End of the Affair

This "singularly moving and beautiful" (Evelyn Waugh) story tells of a man's obsessive behavior when his love affair with a friend's wife is inexplicably broken off by her.

20TH-CENTURY CLASSICS

192 pp.   0-14-018495-3 $ 9.95

England Made Me

A tour de force of moral suspense, this is the story of a confirmed liar and cheat whose untimely discovery of decency may cost him not only his job but also his life.

20TH-CENTURY CLASSICS

208 pp.   0-14-018551-8 $ 9.95

A Gun for Sale

Here is quintessential Graham Greene—the story of a cold-blooded killer on the run, and the violence and double crosses that drive him.

20TH-CENTURY CLASSICS

208 pp.   0-14-018540-2 $ 8.95

The Heart of the Matter

The terrifying depiction of a man's awe of the Church and the ability to portray human motive and to convey such a depth of suffering make *The Heart of the Matter* one of Graham Greene's most enduring, tragic novels.

20TH-CENTURY CLASSICS

272 pp.   0-14-018496-1 $ 9.95

In Search of a Character

For a description, see TRAVEL.

It's a Battlefield

Drover, a communist bus-driver, is in prison appealing a death sentence for killing a policeman who he believed was going to strike his wife in this moving, bitter, tragic, and humorous tale of "the injustice of men's justice."

20TH-CENTURY CLASSICS

208 pp.   0-14-018541-0 $ 9.95

Journey Without Maps

For a description, see TRAVEL.

The Lawless Roads

For a description, see TRAVEL.

The Man Within

The themes of betrayal, pursuit, and the search for peace run through Greene's first published novel about a smuggler who takes refuge from his avengers.

20TH-CENTURY CLASSICS

224 pp.   0-14-018530-5 $ 9.95

May We Borrow Your Husband? And Other Comedies of the Sexual Life

"One of the major writers of his time" (*Newsweek*) offers twelve poignant, shrewd, and sometimes gleeful tales of love and its discontents.

20TH-CENTURY CLASSICS

144 pp.   0-14-018537-2 $ 6.95

The Ministry of Fear

This is a complex portrait of the shadowy inner landscape of Arthur Rowe—torn apart with guilt over mercifully murdering his sick wife—and the terrifying and phantasmagoric landscape of England during the Blitz.

20TH-CENTURY CLASSICS

224 pp.   0-14-018536-4 $ 8.95

Our Man in Havana

In this comical novel, Wormwold tries to keep his job as a secret agent in Havana by filing bogus reports based on Lamb's *Tales from Shakespeare* and dreaming up military installations from vacuum-cleaner designs.

20TH-CENTURY CLASSICS

224 pp.   0-14-018493-7 $ 9.95

The Power and the Glory

Set in a terror-ridden Mexican state, Greene's masterpiece is a compelling depiction of a "whisky priest" struggling to overcome physical and moral cowardice and find redemption.

20TH-CENTURY CLASSICS

224 pp.   0-14-018499-6 $ 9.95

The Quiet American

While the French Army in Indo-China grapples with the Vietminh, a young and high-minded American based in Saigon begins to channel economic aid to a "Third Force" —leading him to blunder into a complex political and cultural world he seems not to understand fully, with disastrous and violent results.

20TH-CENTURY CLASSICS

192 pp.   0-14-018500-3 $ 9.95

Stamboul Train

Green's suspense thriller involves the desperate affair between a pragmatic Jew and a naïve chorus girl, entangled in lust, duplicity, and murder, and set on the Orient Express.

20TH-CENTURY CLASSICS

224 pp.   0-14-018532-1 $ 9.95

The Third Man and The Fallen Idol

This edition pairs two thrillers: Greene's legendary *The Third Man* and *The Fallen Idol*, in which a small boy discovers the deadly truths of the adult world.

20TH-CENTURY CLASSICS

160 pp.   0-14-018533-X $ 8.95

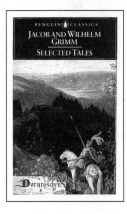

Travels with My Aunt

Henry Pulling's dull suburban life is interrupted when his septuagenarian Aunt Augusta persuades him to travel the world with her in her own inimitable style.

20TH-CENTURY CLASSICS

272 pp.   0-14-018501-1 $ 9.95

ZANE GREY
1875–1939, AMERICAN

Riders of the Purple Sage

Introduced by Jane Tompkins

A great drama of psyche and landscape, Zane Grey's bestselling 1912 adventure romance is the classic Western novel, with popular appeal and distinct codes of chivalry and toughness.

20TH-CENTURY CLASSICS

304 pp.   0-14-018440-6 $ 9.95

JACOB and WILHELM GRIMM
1785–1863; 1786–1859, GERMAN

Selected Tales

Translated and introduced by David Luke

Sixty-five newly translated selections from *Kinder- und Hausmärchen* provide a representative sample of the folktale motifs that have fascinated children and adults around the world for centuries.

432 pp.   0-14-044401-7 $ 9.95

JAMES HANLEY
1901–1985, IRISH

The Furys

Dubliner James Hanley's novel revolves around the Irish Fury family's ambitions, resentments, and brutal disappointments—set against the unrest and poverty of 1926 England.

20TH-CENTURY CLASSICS

400 pp.   0-14-018507-0 $ 11.95

THOMAS HARDY
1840–1928, ENGLISH

The Distracted Preacher and Other Tales
Edited and introduced by Susan Hill

Writing in the latter part of the nineteenth century, Hardy has captured the provincial experiences of his native Dorset and environs. Eleven of his best and most representative stories include "The Withered Arm," "Barbara of the House of Grebe," "The Son's Veto," "A Tragedy of Two Ambitions," and the title story.

368 pp.   0-14-043124-1 $ 6.95

Far from the Madding Crowd
Edited by Ronald Blythe

Hardy's most humorous novel, this book is based on the author's firsthand knowledge of the attitudes, habits, and idiosyncrasies of rural men and women.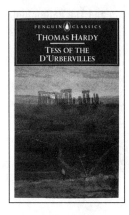

496 pp.   0-14-043126-8 $ 5.95

Jude the Obscure
Edited by C. H. Sisson

In this haunting love story, a couple who have each fled a previous marriage find love and fulfillment together, only to have tragedy overwhelm them.

512 pp.   0-14-043131-4 $ 5.95

The Mayor of Casterbridge
Edited by Martin Seymour-Smith

In this depiction of a man who overreaches the limits allowed by society, Hardy demonstrates his grasp of psychology and of the contradictions inherent in man's nature.

448 pp.   0-14-043125-X $ 5.95

A Pair of Blue Eyes
Edited and introduced by Roger Ebbatson

Modeled on Hardy's own wife, the heroine of this lyrical novel exerts strong influence over men; but her inability to shape her own future ultimately leads to tragedy.

432 pp.   0-14-043266-3 $ 6.95

The Return of the Native
Edited by George Woodcock

Against the menace and beauty of his Wessex landscape, Hardy explores the impersonal forces and eternal verities that control the life of Eustacia Vye and all those around her.

496 pp.   0-14-043122-5 $ 5.95

Tess of the D'Urbervilles
Edited by David Skilton
Introduced by A. Alvarez

In a novel full of poetry and mysteriously luminous settings, Hardy unfolds the story of his most striking and tragic heroine with unforgettable intensity and tenderness.

536 pp.   0-14-043135-7 $ 5.95

The Trumpet-Major

One of Hardy's last novels, this comedy of the Napoleonic Wars contrasts sharply with the tragedies that characterized most of his later works.

320 pp.   0-14-043273-6 $ 6.95

Under the Greenwood Tree

Edited by David Wright

The first of Hardy's Wessex novels, this is a vivid and authentic re-creation of the village, countryside, and people Hardy knew as a child.

256 pp.   0-14-043123-3 $ 5.95

The Woodlanders

Edited by James Gibson
Introduced by Ian Gregor

In this portrait of four people caught up in a web of intense, often unrequited passion, Hardy reveals the complexity of sexual feeling that he was to explore further in *Jude the Obscure*.

464 pp.   0-14-043145-4 $ 5.95

JOEL CHANDLER HARRIS
1848–1908, AMERICAN

Uncle Remus
His Songs and His Sayings

Edited and introduced by
Robert Hemenway

The dialect, lore, and flavor of black life in the nineteenth-century South is portrayed as it appeared to Georgia-born Joel Chandler Harris in Uncle Remus's "Legends of the Old Plantation."

288 pp.   0-14-039014-6 $ 8.95

L. P. HARTLEY
1895–1972, ENGLISH

The Go-Between

This novel—one of the finest portraits of Victorian England—depicts the terrible loss of innocence of a boy who is asked to carry love letters between an aristocratic woman and her lover, a local farmer.

20TH-CENTURY CLASSICS

288 pp.   0-14-018307-8 $ 9.95

JAROSLAV HAŠEK
1883–1923, CZECH

The Good Soldier Svejk

Translated and introduced by
Cecil Parrot

This classic novel portrays the "little man" fighting officialdom and bureaucracy with the only weapons available to him—passive resistance, subterfuge, native wit, and dumb insolence.

20TH-CENTURY CLASSICS

784 pp.   0-14-018274-8 $ 10.95

NATHANIEL HAWTHORNE
1804–1864, AMERICAN

The Blithedale Romance

Introduced by Annette Kolodny

In language that is suggestive and often erotic, Hawthorne offers a superb depiction of a utopian community that cannot survive the individual passions of its members; it is based on his own experiences at Brook Farm.

304 pp.   0-14-039028-6 $ 6.95

Selected Tales and Sketches

Introduced by Michael J. Calacurcio

Displaying Hawthorne's understanding of the distinctly American conscious-ness, these short fictions of the 1820s, 1830s, and 1840s deal with themes that reappear in the *The Scarlet Letter* and his other long works.

484 pp.   0-14-039057-X $ 8.95

WILLIAM HAZLITT
1788–1830, ENGLISH

Selected Writings

Edited and introduced by Ronald Blythe

Writings by the prolific eighteenth-century journalist and essayist Hazlitt are alive with his cantankerous, uncom-promising spirit and his radical protests.

512 pp.   0-14-043050-4 $ 11.95

JOHANN PETER HEBEL
1760–1826, GERMAN

The Treasure Chest

Translated and introduced by John Hibberd

First published in 1811, this collection of jokes, comic anecdotes, sensational murder stories, moral tales, and myster-ies celebrates the ingenuity and cunning of the common man.

208 pp.   0-14-044639-7 $ 10.95

The House of the Seven Gables

Edited and introduced by Milton R. Stern

This enduring novel of crime and retri-bution is a psychological drama that vividly reflects the social and moral val-ues of New England in the 1840s.

352 pp.   0-14-039005-7 $ 8.95

The Marble Faun

Introduced by Richard H. Brodhead

Set in Rome, Hawthorne's tale of the in-fluence of European culture on Ameri-can morality echoes *The Scarlet Letter* in its concern with the nature of trans-gression and guilt.

480 pp.   0-14-039077-4 $ 8.95

The Scarlet Letter

Introduced by Nina Baym

Hawthorne's classic novel of guilt and redemption in pre-Revolutionary Mass-achussetts provides vivid insight into the social and religious forces that shaped early America.

256 pp.   0-14-039019-7 $ 5.95

HEINRICH HEINE
1797–1856, GERMAN

Selected Prose

Edited, translated, and introduced by Ritchie Robertson

This collection of extraordinary prose—meditations on spiritualism and sensualism, evocative travel narratives, memoirs of his Jewish childhood, and much more—exemplifies the artistry of German poet Heinrich Heine, best known for the poems adopted as song texts by musicians Schubert and Brahms.

368 pp.   0-14-044555-2 $ 11.95

O. HENRY
1862–1918, AMERICAN

Cabbages and Kings

Introduced with notes by Guy Davenport

Cabbages and Kings is the first book, and the only novel, by O. Henry, the famed satirist and unabashed middle-class moralist of the American comic tradition.

20TH-CENTURY CLASSICS
288 pp.   0-14-018689-1 $ 10.95

Selected Stories

Edited and introduced by Guy Davenport

Compiled here are eighty classic stories about con men, tricksters, and innocent deceivers, about fate, luck, and coincidence, by one of the great masters of American literary comedy and the short story form.

20TH-CENTURY CLASSICS
384 pp.   0-14-018688-3 $ 11.95

ERNST THEODOR HOFFMANN
1776–1822, GERMAN

The Tales of Hoffmann

Translated by R. J. Hollingdale

Eight of Hoffmann's best and best-known tales are retold in this collection—among them "Mademoiselle de Scudery," "Doge and Dogeressa," and "The Sandman," which forms the basis for the first half of Offenbach's opera.

416 pp.   0-14-044392-4 $ 9.95

JAMES HOGG
1770–1835, SCOTTISH

The Private Memoirs and Confessions of a Justified Sinner

Edited and introduced by John Wain

Through a supernatural tale in which the Calvinist doctrine of predestination allows a devout young man to rationalize murder, James Hogg reflects the moral and religious tensions of early nineteenth-century British society.

256 pp.   0-14-043198-5 $ 8.95

The Iliad

Introduced with noted by Bernard Knox
Translated by Robert Fagles

Robert Fagles combines his talents as poet and scholar to present this masterful, elegant new translation of the stirring story of the Trojan War and the rage of Achilles. "An astonishing performance. There is no modern version of the whole *Iliad* which is better or as good, and this should now become the standard translation for a new generation." —Peter Levi

672 pp.   0-14-044592-7 $ 8.95

The Iliad
A New Prose Translation

Translated and introduced by
Martin Hammond

This prose translation captures the emotional power and the dramatic tension of the first and greatest literary achievement of Greek civilization.

416 pp.   0-14-044444-0 $ 8.95

The Odyssey

Translated by E. V. Rieu
Revised translation by D. C. H. Rieu

Odysseus' perilous ten-year voyage from Troy to his home in Ithaca is recounted in a revised translation that captures the swiftness, drama, and worldview of the Greek original.

448 pp.   0-14-044556-0 $ 8.95

A Modern Instance

Introduced by Edwin H. Cady

The story of a philandering, dishonest Boston journalist and the woman who divorces him, this is the first serious treatment of divorce in American writing and a powerful example of realism in literature.

480 pp.   0-14-039027-8 $ 7.95

The Rise of Silas Lapham

Introduced by Kermit Vanderbilt

The social and moral questions posed by the Gilded Age of American business are chronicled in this tale of a newly rich New England family.

352 pp.   0-14-039030-8 $ 9.95

VICTOR HUGO
1802–1885, FRENCH

Les Misérables
Translated and introduced by Norman Denny

Including unforgettable descriptions of the Paris sewers, the battle of Waterloo, and the fighting at the barricades during the July Revolution, this is at once a thrilling narrative and a vivid social document. 🖽

1,248 pp.   0-14-044430-0 $ 9.95

Nôtre-Dame of Paris
Translated and introduced by John Sturrock

Hugo's powerful evocation of Paris in 1482 and the tragic tale of Quasimodo has become the classic example of French romanticism.

496 pp.   0-14-044353-3 $ 9.95

J. K. HUYSMANS
1848–1907, FRENCH

Against Nature
Translated by Robert Baldick

This chronicle of the exotic practices and perverse pleasures of a hero who is a thinly disguised version of the author was condemned by the public as a work of alarming depravity—and much admired by Oscar Wilde.

224 pp.   0-14-044086-0 $ 9.95

HENRY JAMES
1843–1916, AMERICAN

The Ambassadors
Edited and introduced by Harry Levin

One of Henry James's three final novels, this tale, set in Paris, is a finely drawn portrait of a man's late awakening to the importance of morality.

520 pp.   0-14-043233-7 $ 4.95

The American
Edited and introduced by William Spengemann

This story of an American millionaire rejected by the family of the European aristocrat he loves is James's first novel to dramatize the social relationship between the Old World and the New.

392 pp.   0-14-039082-0 $ 8.95

The American Scene
For a description see TRAVEL.

The Aspern Papers and The Turn of the Screw
Edited and introduced with notes by Anthony Curtis

Set in a palazzo in Venice, *The Aspern Papers* tells of the confrontation between an elderly woman and a charming young man; in *The Turn of the Screw*, the story of a governess and her charges, James conjures up inexplicable terrors.

272 pp.   0-14-043224-8 $ 4.95

The Awkward Age

Edited and introduced by Ronald Blythe

This study of innocence exposed to corrupting influences has been praised for its natural dialogue and the delicacy of feeling it conveys.

328 pp.   0-14-043297-3 $ 8.95

The Bostonians

Edited and introduced with notes by Charles Anderson

In this story of a Mississippi lawyer, a radical feminist, and their struggle for exclusive possession of a beautiful woman, James explores what it means to be fully human, for both men and women.

464 pp.   0-14-043225-6 $ 4.95

Daisy Miller

Edited and introduced by Geoffrey Moore

James's first novel to reach great popularity, this is also the first of his great portraits of an American woman.

128 pp.   0-14-043262-0 $ 3.95

The Europeans

Edited and introduced by Tony Tanner

This subtle examination of the effect of two slightly raffish Europeans upon their cousins in rural Boston in 1830 was published the year after James's *The American.*

576 pp.   0-14-043232-9 $ 3.95

The Figure in the Carpet and Other Stories

Edited and introduced with notes by Frank Kermode

James's first short story, launched in 1864, was followed, throughout his varied literary career, by nearly a hundred more. This sampling includes "The Author of Beltraffio," "The Lesson of the Master," "The Private Life," "The Middle Years," "The Death of the Lion," "The New Time," "The Figure in the Carpet," and "John Delavoy."

464 pp.   0-14-043255-8 $ 8.95

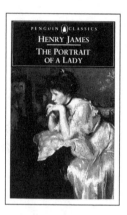

The Golden Bowl

Introduced by Gore Vidal

A work unique among James's novels in that things come out right for the characters, this is the story of the alliance between Italian aristocracy and American millionaires.

576 pp.   0-14-043235-3 $ 5.95

An International Episode and Other Stories

Edited and introduced by S. Gorley Putt

"An International Episode," "The Pension Beaurepas," and "Lady Barberina" all deal with the relations—embarrassing, amusing, and at times tender—between Americans and the English.

224 pp.   0-14-043227-2 $ 8.95

Italian Hours

For a description see TRAVEL.

The Jolly Corner and Other Tales

Edited and introduced by Roger Gard

All written after 1900, these stories share the themes and moods that best illustrate James's late style. The selection includes "The Third Person," "Broken Wings," "The Beast in the Jungle," "The Birthplace," "The Jolly Corner," "The Velvet Glove," "Crapy Cornelia," and "The Bench of Desolation."

320 pp.   0-14-043328-7 $ 9.95

A Landscape-Painter and Other Tales: 1864–1874

Edited and introduced by Roger Gard

James's experimentation with the short story form was broadened and rewarded by his frequent contributions to literary journals, culminating in his being one of the original proponents of stream of consciousness writing. Included here are additional representations of his art: "The Story of the Year," "A Landscape-Painter," "A Day of Days," "A Light Man," "Master Eustace," "The Sweetheart of M. Briseux," "Madame de Mauves," and "Professor Fargo."

336 pp.   0-14-043327-9 $ 6.95

The Portrait of a Lady

Edited and introduced by Geoffrey Moore

Regarded by many critics as James's masterpiece, this is the story of Isabel Archer, an independent American heiress captivated by the languid charms of an Englishman.

688 pp.   0-14-043223-X $ 5.95

The Princess Casamassima

Edited and introduced by Derek Brewer

A young man involved in the world of revolutionary politics falls in love with the beautiful Princess Casamassima and finds he must make a choice between his honor and his desires.

608 pp.   0-14-043254-X $ 9.95

Roderick Hudson

Edited and introduced by Geoffrey Moore

In his first full-length novel James writes with verve and passion about an egotistical young sculptor and the mentor who tries to help him develop his talents.

400 pp.   0-14-043264-7 $ 5.95

The Sacred Fount

Edited and introduced by John Lyon

Disconcerting, outrageous, perhaps even a Jamesian joke, *The Sacred Fount* is certainly James's most audacious work of fiction, evoking an esoteric, idiosyncratic world where the author is fully in control.

240 pp.   0-14-043350-3 $ 10.95

The Spoils of Poynton

Edited and introduced by David Lodge

In this study of irreducible ambiguity, a family quarrel unfolds when a woman and her son disagree on whom he should marry and one of the potential brides will not make her true feelings known.

256 pp.   0-14-043288-4 $ 8.95

The Tragic Muse

Edited and introduced by Philip Horne

Henry James explores the tensions between the artistic life and worldly temptations in a novel at once satiric and serious. He muses on the concept of "art for art's sake," on the vagaries of society's infatuation with the artist, and, as he writes in his preface, on "the personal consequences of the art-appetite raised to intensity, swollen to voracity."

576 pp.   0-14-043389-9 $ 12.95

Washington Square

Edited and introduced with notes by Brian Lee

This early novel, set in New York, is a spare and intensely moving story of divided loyalties and innocence betrayed.

224 pp.   0-14-043226-4 $ 4.95

What Maisie Knew

Edited and introduced by Paul Theroux

In creating a portrait of a young girl raised in a world of intrigue and betrayal, James sketches with subtle irony the actions and motives of her corrupt adult companions.

288 pp.   0-14-043248-5 $ 4.95

Wings of the Dove

Edited and introduced by John Bayley

The story of a rich, lonely, and gravely ill young woman searching for happiness, this beautifully written novel deals with human greed and human tragedy.

520 pp.   0-14-043263-9 $ 5.95

JAMES WELDON JOHNSON
1871–1938, AMERICAN

Along This Way
The Autobiography of James Weldon Johnson

For a description, see AUTOBIOGRAPHY AND BIOGRAPHY.

The Autobiography of an Ex-Colored Man

Introduced by William L. Andrews

First published in 1912, Johnson's pioneering fictional "memoir" is an unprecedented analysis of the social causes and artistic consequences of a black man's denial of his heritage.

20TH-CENTURY CLASSICS

304 pp.   0-14-018402-3 $ 7.95

God's Trombones

For a description, see POETRY.

Saint Peter Relates an Incident

For a description, see POETRY.

SAMUEL JOHNSON
1709–1784, ENGLISH

The History of Rasselas, Prince of Abissinia

Edited by D. J. Enright

The pilgrimage of Rasselas from Abissinia to Egypt is used as a vehicle for Johnson's musings on such wide-ranging subjects as flying machines, poetry, marriage, and madness.

160 pp.   0-14-043108-X $ 7.95

Selected Writings

Edited and introduced by Patrick Crutwell

Generous selections from Johnson's major works include *A Journey to the Western Islands of Scotland*, *The Dictionary of the English Language*, and *The Lives of the English Poets*, as well as portions of his journals, letters, and papers.

576 pp.   0-14-043033-4 $ 10.95

JAMES JOYCE
1882–1941, IRISH

Dubliners

Introduced with notes by Terence Brown

In these stories about the men and women of the struggling lower middle-class and their anxious desires for respectability, Joyce creates an exacting portrait and a lament for his native city and Irish culture.

20TH-CENTURY CLASSICS
368 pp.   0-14-018647-6 $ 7.95

A Portrait of the Artist as a Young Man

Edited and introduced with notes by Seamus Deane

Joyce's rich and complex coming-of-age story of the artist Stephen Dedalus— one of the great portraits of modern "Irishness"— is a tour de force of style and technique.

20TH-CENTURY CLASSICS
384 pp.   0-14-018683-2 $ 7.95

FRANZ KAFKA
1833–1924, CZECH

The Transformation ("Metamorphosis") and Other Stories

Translated and edited by Malcolm Pasley

This collection of all the works published during Kafka's lifetime includes "The Transformation," Kafka's famous story of a man who wakes to find himself trapped in the body of an insect; the author's 1909 account of an air show; selections from *Meditation*; "The Stroker," a fragment from a novel set in America; "Before the Law," the only part of *The Trial* published during Kafka's lifetime; "In the Penal Colony"; and other stories from *The Fasting Artist* written shortly before his death.

20TH-CENTURY CLASSICS
256 pp.   0-14-018478-3 $ 10.95

JACK KEROUAC
1922–1969, AMERICAN

On the Road
Introduced by Ann Charters

The novel that defined the Beat generation, this exuberant tale of Sal Paradise
and Dean Moriarty traversing America
swings to the rhythms of the 1950s. 🖥
20TH-CENTURY CLASSICS

316 pp.   0-14-018521-6 $ 10.95

RUDYARD KIPLING
1865–1936, ENGLISH

The Day's Work
*Edited and introduced by
Constantine Phipps*

Kipling's grasp of the complexities of
Colonial rule in India infuse the stories
he wrote about the land of his birth.
These twelve, first published in 1898, in-
clude "The Bridge Builders" and "The
Maltese Cat."

336 pp.   0-14-043312-0 $ 5.95

A Diversity of Creatures
Edited and introduced by Paul Driver

This commanding collection of stories
and poems by the first English writer to
win the Nobel Prize for Literature includes "As Easy as A.B.C," "The Village
That Voted the Earth Was Flat," and
many others.
20TH-CENTURY CLASSICS

368 pp.   0-14-018694-8 $ 10.95

The Jungle Books
Edited and introduced by Daniel Karlin

Kipling's knowledge of and love for the
jungle animates these delightful fables,
many featuring Mowgli the wolfboy;
both *The Jungle Book* and *The Second
Jungle Book* are included in this volume.
20TH-CENTURY CLASSICS

384 pp.   0-14-018316-7 $ 6.95

Just-So Stories
Edited and introduced by Peter Levi

Linked by poems and scattered with
Kipling's own illustrations, these imaginative fables were inspired by the author's empathy with the animal world
and his delight with the foibles of human nature.
20TH-CENTURY CLASSICS

128 pp.   0-14-018351-5 $ 4.95

Kim
Edited and introduced by Edward Said

The story of a young boy who moves
through two cultures, Kim captures India's opulent, exotic landscape, over-
shadowed by the uneasy presence of
British rule.
20TH-CENTURY CLASSICS

320 pp.   0-14-018352-3 $ 3.95

Life's Handicap
Being Stories of My Own People
*Edited and introduced with notes by
P. N. Furbank*

First published in 1891, these twenty-
seven zestful, youthful stories fore-
shadow Kipling's mature talents.

304 pp.   0-14-043279-5 $ 5.95

The Light That Failed

Edited and introduced by John Lyon

Powerful and haunting, this novel of an artist and writer facing tragedy—the loss of creativity, sight, and love—demonstrates the energy and force of Kipling's own vision.

20TH-CENTURY CLASSICS

242 pp.   0-14-018512-7 $ 8.95

RUDYARD KIPLING
Just So Stories

Plain Tales from the Hills

Edited by H. R. Woudhuysen
Introduced with notes by David Trotter

Originally intended for a provincial readership familiar with colonial life, these stories of "heat and bewilderment and wasted effort and broken faith" were later revised by the author for the English edition—to re-create the sights and smells of India.

20TH-CENTURY CLASSICS

288 pp.   0-14-018312-4 $ 7.95

Puck of Pook's Hill

Edited and introduced by Sarah Wintle

In this classic combining Kipling's interests in the supernatural and English history, two children act out their own version of *A Midsummer Night's Dream* and miraculously conjure up Puck himself.

20TH-CENTURY CLASSICS

208 pp.   0-14-018353-1 $ 8.95

Rewards and Fairies

Edited and introduced by Roger Lewis

A classic collection of stories that can be enjoyed on many levels, *Rewards and Fairies* continues the adventures, begun in *Puck of Pook's Hill*, of the last surviving fairy in England.

20TH-CENTURY CLASSICS

304 pp.   0-14-018437-6 $ 8.95

Soldiers Three
and In Black and White

Introduced by Salman Rushdie

Stories of British India told from a romantic foreigner's perspective, and from the Indian's point of view—these Kipling tales reveal the ambiguous, shifting relationship between England and India.

20TH-CENTURY CLASSICS

240 pp.   0-14-018289-6 $ 9.95

Traffics and Discoveries

Edited and introduced by Hermione Lee

These twenty-two poems and stories by Kipling are a testimony to his zest for narrative, his sense of history, and his daring breadth of imagination. The collection includes "The Captive," on the ambiguities of war.

20TH-CENTURY CLASSICS

1,352 pp.   0-14-018375-2 $ 9.95

Wee Willie Winkie

Edited and introduced by Hugh Haughton

These fourteen stories evolved during Kipling's last year in India, and are taken from *Under the Deodars*, *Wee Willie Winkie*, and *The Phantom Rickshaw* (which includes "The Man Who Would Be King" and "The Strange Ride of Morrowbie Jukes").

20TH-CENTURY CLASSICS

432 pp.   0-14-018380-9 $ 9.95

HEINRICH VON KLEIST
1777–1811, GERMAN

The Marquise of O and Other Stories

Translated and introduced by David Luke and Nigel Reeves

This collection of works from the last period of Kleist's life includes "The Earthquake in Chile," "Michael Kohlhaas," "The Beggarwoman of Locarno," "St. Cecilia or The Power of Music," "The Betrothal in Santo Domingo," "The Foundling," and "The Duel."

320 pp.   0-14-044359-2 $ 8.95

WOLFGANG KOEPPEN
B.1906, GERMAN

Death in Rome

Translated and introduced by Michael Hoffman

Wolfgang Koeppen, one of Germany's greatest living authors, writes a haunting allegory of the shame and legacy of Germany's Nazi past, following two fathers and their sons—one a priest, one a composer—who represent the contested soul of Germany.

20TH-CENTURY CLASSICS

224 pp.   0-14-018790-1 $ 10.95

ARTHUR KOESTLER
1905–1983, HUNGARIAN

Arrival and Departure

"Koestler is one of the very few novelists who attacks the most difficult and troubling issues of private and political morality and who, having raised serious questions, never tries to satisfy us with ready-made answers or evasions."
—Saul Bellow

20TH-CENTURY CLASSICS

192 pp.   0-14-018119-9 $ 7.95

JEAN DE LA FONTAINE
1621–1695, FRENCH

Selected Fables

Translated by James Michie

Although he drew from Aesop, *Phaedrus*, and the Persians, La Fontaine reinvented the fable in verses full of irresistible freshness.

176 pp.   0-14-044376-2 $ 8.95

CHODERLOS DE LACLOS
1741–1803, FRENCH

Les Liaisons Dangereuses
Translated by P. W. K. Stone

One of the most notorious novels of all time, this eighteenth-century work describes the intrigues of a depraved pair of aristocrats plotting the seduction of a young convent girl.

400 pp.   0-14-044116-6 $ 6.95

MADAME DE LAFAYETTE
1634–1693, FRENCH

The Princesse de Clèves
*Translated and introduced by
Robin Buss*

One of the first feminist novels, this romance about a woman's dangerous but platonic liaison is a milestone of French literature, and a precursor to the psychological realism of Proust.

192 pp.   0-14-044587-0 $ 8.95

WILLIAM LANGLAND
c. 1330–c. 1400, ENGLISH

Piers the Ploughman
Translated by J. F. Goodridge

Written by a fourteenth-century cleric, this spiritual allegory explores man in relation to his ultimate destiny against the background of teeming, colorful medieval life.

320 pp.   0-14-044087-9 $ 9.95

D. H. LAWRENCE
1885–1930, ENGLISH

Apocalypse
Introduced by Richard Aldington

In Lawrence's last work, he launches a fierce protest against Christianity and science while simultaneously celebrating the human spirit.

20TH-CENTURY CLASSICS
160 pp.   0-14-018197-0 $ 8.95

The Boy in the Bush
This story of a handsome vagabond learning to survive in the harsh Australian bush celebrates nature at its most redemptively inhuman.

20TH-CENTURY CLASSICS
400 pp.   0-14-018446-5 $ 9.95

Complete Poems
For a description, see POETRY.

England, My England
Echoes of the First World War resound in ten stories that include "The Blind Man," "Wintry Peacock," "The Primrose Path," and "Fannie and Annie."

20TH-CENTURY CLASSICS
192 pp.   0-14-018198-9 $ 9.95

The Fox, The Captain's Doll, The Ladybird

Edited by Dieter Mehl
Introduced with notes by David Ellis

Set during and after the First World War, these three short novels feature struggles between men and women, a theme common to much of Lawrence's work.

20TH-CENTURY CLASSICS

272 pp.   0-14-018779-0 $ 9.95

John Thomas and Lady Jane

This is the second of three versions of Lawrence's controversial *Lady Chatterley's Lover;* both the characters and the development of the love story are quite different from the final version.

20TH-CENTURY CLASSICS

376 pp.   0-14-018200-4 $ 9.95

Kangaroo

At the end of World War I, an English couple flee the exhaustion of Europe for the rough vitality of Australia, where they fall under the spell of a magnetic but dangerous political leader.

20TH-CENTURY CLASSICS

400 pp.   0-14-018201-2 $ 9.95

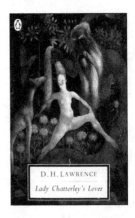

D. H. LAWRENCE
Lady Chatterley's Lover

Lady Chatterley's Lover

Edited and introduced with notes by Michael Squires

This restored text of Lawrence's most famous work explicitly chronicles the affair between Constance Chatterley and the gamekeeper Mellors and includes the author's "À Propos of Lady Chatterley's Lover," his final thoughts on the male-female relationship in the modern world.

20TH-CENTURY CLASSICS

400 pp.   0-14-018786-3 $ 9.95

The Lost Girl

In this rendering of English provincial life, Lawrence creates a heroine who rebels against the ordinariness of her life and finally seeks escape in Italy.

20TH-CENTURY CLASSICS

400 pp.   0-14-018206-3 $ 7.95

Love Among the Haystacks and Other Stories

Originally published near the time of Lawrence's death in 1930, this collection of short stories explores themes of human isolation and relationships. It includes the title story, "The Lovely Lad," "The Man Who Loved Islands," and three other tales.

20TH-CENTURY CLASSICS
176 pp.   0-14-018203-9 $ 8.95

The Prussian Officer

Written between 1907 and 1914, these twelve stories illuminate Lawrence's increasing interest in the conflict between immediate human experience and the eternal, impersonal forces that operate at the level of the unconscious.

20TH-CENTURY CLASSICS
304 pp.   0-14-018780-4 $ 10.95

The Rainbow

Based on Lawrence's original manuscript of the generational saga of the Brangwen family, this new Cambridge text features a specially commissioned introduction, notes on the text, and suggestions for further reading.

20TH-CENTURY CLASSICS
528 pp.   0-14-018813-4 $ 7.95

Sons and Lovers

Edited and introduced with notes by Helen Baron and Carl Baron

Presented in paperback for the first time in its complete form, including the restoration of eighty pages missing from previous editions, *Sons and Lovers* examines the tensions in the Morel family as the world around them moves from the agricultural past to the industrial future and their own dreams and illusions change.

20TH-CENTURY CLASSICS
544 pp.   0-14-018832-0 $ 9.95

The Trespasser

Edited by Elizabeth Mansfield
Introduced with notes by John Turner

This second novel of Lawrence's tells a tale of love outside marriage and its tragic consequences as it follows the unhappy musician Siemund, who, in a desperate bid for his freedom, ultimately begins a further descent into confusion and despair.

20TH-CENTURY CLASSICS
288 pp.   0-14-018800-2 $ 9.95

The White Peacock

Published in 1911 and strongly autobiographical in content, Lawrence's first novel reveals his innovative style and explores the conflicts of class, morality, and sexuality that would continue to inform his later work.

20TH-CENTURY CLASSICS
416 pp.   0-14-018778-2 $ 9.95

The Woman Who Rode Away and Other Stories

Introduced by Richard Aldington

A diverse collection of twelve stories by the admired and moody Lawrence includes several works of satire, a tale of ghosts and the occult, and stories of dark powers and sensual awakenings.

20TH-CENTURY CLASSICS

256 pp.   0-14-018212-8 $ 9.95

Women in Love

Edited by David Farmer, Lindeth Vasey, and John Worthen
Introduced with a note by Mark Kinkhead-Weekes

Considered by many critics to be Lawrence's masterpiece, *Women in Love* is a powerful, sexually explicit depiction of the destructiveness of human relations. 📖

20TH-CENTURY CLASSICS

592 pp.   0-14-018816-9 $ 9.95

MIKHAIL LERMONTOV
1814–1841, RUSSIAN

A Hero of Our Time

Translated by Paul Foote

Lermontov's portrait of a cynical, flamboyant man is an early landmark in Russian literature, one that influenced Tolstoy, Dostoyevsky, Chekhov, and other nineteenth-century masters.

192 pp.   0-14-044176-X $ 8.95

NIKOLAI LESKOV
1831–1895, RUSSIAN

Lady Macbeth of Mtsensk and Other Stories

Translated and introduced by David McDuff

A pervasive religious spirit combined with lurid dashes of intrigue and carefully detailed descriptions of nineteenth-century peasant life characterize the work of one of Russia's most important—though long-neglected—authors. This selection includes "The Sealed Angel," "Pamphalon the Entertainer," "Musk-Ox," and "A Winter's Day."

432 pp.   0-14-044491-2 $ 10.95

PRIMO LEVI
1919–1987, ITALIAN

If Not Now, When?

Introduced by Irving Howe
Translated by William Weaver

Based on a true story, this powerful book is a moving tribute to the strength and ingenuity of the human spirit.

20TH-CENTURY CLASSICS

356 pp.   0-14-018893-2 $ 11.95

Moments of Reprieve

For a description, see AUTOBIOGRAPHY AND BIOGRAPHY.

The Monkey's Wrench

Translated by Ruth Feldman

This exuberant and funny novel, an enchanting collection of tales told between a self-educated construction worker and a writer-chemist, celebrates the joys of work and the art of storytelling.

20TH-CENTURY CLASSICS

176 pp.   0-14-018892-4 $ 10.95

SINCLAIR LEWIS
1885–1951, AMERICAN

Main Street

Introduced by Martin Bucco

Main Street, Sinclair Lewis's portrait of Gopher Prairie, Minnesota, shattered the myth of the Middle West as God's country and became a symbol of the cultural narrow-mindedness and smug complacency of small towns everywhere.

20TH-CENTURY CLASSICS

448 pp.   0-14-018901-7 $ 9.95

WYNDHAM LEWIS
1884–1957, ENGLISH

Tarr

Drawn from his youthful life in Bohemian Paris in the early 1900s, Lewis's comic first novel explores the relationship of the artist to art and sexuality, proving "a masterpiece of the period" (V. S. Pritchett).

20TH-CENTURY CLASSICS

336 pp.   0-14-018264-0 $ 9.95

JACK LONDON
1876–1916, AMEIRCAN

The Assassination Bureau, Ltd.

Introduced by Donald Pease

London's unfinished suspense thriller, completed by novelist Robert L. Fish, focuses on the fine distinction between state-justified murder and criminal violence in the Assassination Bureau —an organization whose mandate is to rid the state of all its enemies.

20TH-CENTURY CLASSICS

208 pp.   0-14-018677-8 $ 8.95

The Call of the Wild, White Fang, and Other Stories

Edited by Andrew Sinclair
Introduced by James Dickey

This volume contains the best of London's famed adventure stories of the North, including the mythic *Call of the Wild*, a vivid tale of a dog's fight for survival in the Yukon wilderness, and *White Fang*, the story of a wild dog's acclimation to the world of men.

20TH-CENTURY CLASSICS

416 pp.   0-14-018651-4 $ 7.95

Martin Eden

This semi-autobiographical work depicts a young seaman's struggle for education and literary fame, and his eventual disillusionment with success.

20TH-CENTURY CLASSICS

480 pp.   0-14-018772-3 $ 9.95

The Sea-Wolf and Other Stories

Selected and introduced by
Andrew Sinclair

In the title story London writes of an old sea captain who attempts to put the theories of Spencer and Nietzsche into practice; also included here are "The Sea-Farmer" and "Samuel."

20TH-CENTURY CLASSICS
320 pp.   0-14-018357-4 $ 8.95

Tales of the Pacific

Introduced with an afterword by
Andrew Sinclair

At once rugged and deeply philosophical, these stories depict man's struggle for survival battling not only the elements and the dangers of the great ocean but also the stark cruelty that is bondage, disease, hypocrisy, and secret sin.

20TH-CENTURY CLASSICS
240 pp.   0-14-018358-2 $ 9.95

LONGUS
1ST CENT. A.D., GREEK

Daphnis and Chloë

Translated and introduced by
Paul Turner

At the heart of much romantic literature of the modern era, this physically explicit and emotionally charged early novel holds an important place in the Classic/European canon.

128 pp.   0-14-044059-3 $ 9.95

ANITA LOOS
1893–1981, AMERICAN

But Gentlemen Marry Brunettes

In her entertaining exposé of the literati of New York, Anita Loos continues the adventures of the quintessential blonde, glamour girl Lorelei Lee, who has married her millionaire and relocated from Hollywood to New York in search of new worlds to conquer.

20TH-CENTURY CLASSICS
96 pp.   0-14-018488-0 $ 7.95

Gentlemen Prefer Blondes

This brilliant satire of the Jazz Age and of rags-to-riches American dreamers introduced Lorelei Lee—the glamorous blond flapper from Little Rock—and her adventurous searches for champagne, diamonds, and marriageable millionaires.

20TH-CENTURY CLASSICS
160 pp.   0-14-018487-2 $ 8.95

JOACHIM MARÍA MACHADO DE ASSIS
1839–1908, BRAZILIAN

Dom Casmurro

Translated and introduced by
Robert Scott-Buccleuch

First published in Brazil in 1899, Dom Casmurro tells a tale of the tragedy of love and painful disillusionment and ranks among the most important novels ever written in the Portuguese language.

224 pp.   0-14-044612-5 $ 10.95

Sinister Street

A magnificent portrayal of a young man's coming of age, in which a liaison with a fascinating and destructive woman shows Michael Fane that his future lies in his own hands.

20TH-CENTURY CLASSICS

832 pp.   0-14-018475-9 $ 10.95

BERNARD MALAMUD
1914–1986, AMERICAN

Dubin's Lives

The scene opens on the late middle-age of William Dubin, prizewinning biographer and muddled family man who has lost himself and all his bearings. His return and his possible redemption come only after he tempts fate in out-of-the-ordinary ways.

20TH-CENTURY CLASSICS

400 pp.   0-14-018760-X $ 10.95

The Fixer

Based on the actual case of a Jewish Russian worker accused of murder in Kiev, The Fixer probes into themes common in Malamud's acclaimed work: the solitude of man ostracized by society, and the conflicted legacies of the Jewish people.

20TH-CENTURY CLASSICS

304 pp.   0-14-018515-1 $ 9.95

God's Grace

A fable at once absurd and profound about a sole survivor—with a tamed chimpanzee—of a nuclear holocaust, God's Grace combines "Miltonic ambition and theme with the vernacular crackle of comic dialogue" (The Washington Post).

20TH-CENTURY CLASSICS

208 pp.   0-14-018491-0 $ 9.95

A New Life

Suppressing both fear and self-pity, Sy Levin, a recovering alcoholic, is beginning a new life as an English instructor in the Pacific Northwest, hoping to find peace and renewal. Instead he finds himself the lone liberal fighting a reactionary administration, a crusade made only slightly less onerous by the promise of love—and sex—offered by young students and faculty wives.

20TH-CENTURY CLASSICS

208 pp.   0-14-018681-6 $ 9.95

The Tenants

Malamud's brilliant and ruthlessly funny dissection exposes the relationship between two writers—Harry Lesser, who struggles with his unfinished novel, and Spearmint, the defiant black writer of a violent, anti-Semitic work-in-progress.

20TH-CENTURY CLASSICS

176 pp.   0-14-018516-X $ 9.95

SIR THOMAS MALORY
C. 15TH CENT., ENGLISH

Le Morte d'Arthur
Edited by Janet Cowen

One of the most readable and moving accounts of the Knights of the Round Table, this version of the Arthurian legend was edited and first published by William Caxton in 1485.

Vol. 1: 494 pp. 0-14-043043-1 $ 6.95
Vol. 2: 554 pp. 0-14-043044-1 $ 6.95

OSIP MANDELSTAM
1891–1938, RUSSIAN

The Noise of Time
The Prose of Osip Mandelstam
Translated with critical essays by Clarence Brown

These twenty-nine powerful prose works by the pre-eminent Russian poet of the twentieth century are accompanied by essays placing them in the context of Mandelstam's life and work.

20TH-CENTURY CLASSICS
256 pp. 0-14-018706-5 $ 9.95

BERNARD MANDEVILLE
1670–1733, DUTCH

The Fable of the Bees
For a description, see ECONOMICS.

DELARIVIER MANLEY
1663–1724, ENGLISH

The New Atalantis
Edited and introduced by Ros Ballaster

This major imaginative work—part autobiography and part exposé—was suppressed upon publication in 1709. Manley's erotic and satiric tour of Atalantis was as much an indictment of her society as it is of ours today.

336 pp. 0-14-043370-8 $ 11.95

HEINRICH MANN
1871–1950, GERMAN

Man of Straw
By the elder brother of Thomas Mann, this 1918 novel about a self-adoring brutal leader was a prescient and fierce satire of German militarism, which led to the author's imprisonment.

20TH-CENTURY CLASSICS
304 pp. 0-14-018137-7 $ 9.95

KLAUS MANN
1906–1949, GERMAN

Mephisto
Translated by Robyn Smyth

Mephisto is the story of an actor who, obsessed with fame and power, renounces his communist past and deserts his wife and mistress to continue performing in Nazi Germany. The moral consequences of his betrayals eventually haunt him, turning his dreamworld into a nightmare.

20TH-CENTURY CLASSICS
272 pp. 0-14-018918-1 $ 11.95

FREDERIC MANNING
1882–1935, AUSTRALIAN

The Middle Parts of Fortune

Introduced by Paul Fussell

Hailed as the ultimate novel of trench warfare by Eliot, Pound, and T. E. Lawrence, the story of Private Bourne and his comrades-in-arms is now considered one of the literary masterpieces of the First World War. "The finest and noblest book of war that I have ever read." —Ernest Hemingway

20TH-CENTURY CLASSICS

256 pp.　　0-14-018461-9　　$ 8.95

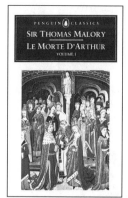

KATHERINE MANSFIELD
1888–1923, NEW ZEALANDER

In a German Pension

Introduced with notes by John Middleton Murry

Mansfield's first published works, these satirical sketches of the early twentieth-century German bourgeoisie at leisure offer a remarkable introduction to the voice of an independent woman breaking free of the constraints of her Victorian upbringing.

20TH-CENTURY CLASSICS

128 pp.　　0-14-018149-0　　$ 6.95

ALESSANDRO MANZONI
1785–1873, ITALIAN

The Betrothed
(I Promessi Sposi)

Translated and introduced by Bruce Penman

In one of the masterpieces of Italian literature, Manzoni chronicles the perils of two lovers caught in the turbulence of seventeenth-century Italy.

720 pp.　　0-14-044274-X　　$ 10.95

MARGUERITE DE NAVARRE
1492–1549, BASQUE

The Heptameron

Translated and introduced by Paul A. Chilton

Inspired by a royal project to produce a French *Decameron*, these seventy stories mirroring Renaissance France's version of the battle of the sexes are attributed to Rabelais's patron, the sister of François I.

544 pp.　　0-14-044355-X　　$ 12.95

Collected Short Stories (4 volumes)
Volume 1

These thirty stories, including the piece "Rain," are set in the Pacific Islands, in England, France, and Spain.

20TH-CENTURY CLASSICS

448 pp.   0-14-018589-5 $ 9.95

Volume 2

The stories collected here, including "The Alien Corn," "Flotsam and Jetsam," and "The Vessel of Wrath," reconfirm Maugham's stature as one of the masters of the short story.

20TH-CENTURY CLASSICS

256 pp.   0-14-018590-9 $ 10.95

Volume 3
Formerly titled Ashenden

Maugham learned his craft from de Maupassant, and these stories display the unique and remarkable talent that made him an unsurpassed storyteller.

20TH-CENTURY CLASSICS

256 pp.   0-14-018591-7 $ 10.95

Volume 4

These thirty stories—most set in the colonies at a time when the Empire was still assured, in a world in which men and women were caught between their own essentially European values and the richness and ambiguity of their unfamiliar surroundings—show a master of the genre at the peak of his power.

20TH-CENTURY CLASSICS

464 pp.   0-14-018592-5 $ 11.95

MARIE DE FRANCE
12TH CENT., FRENCH

The Lais of Marie de France

Translated and introduced by Glyn S. Burgess and Keith Busby

Twelve short story-poems are based on Breton tales of love in crisis, presented in plain prose translations as close to the twelfth-century original as possible. The volume includes the Old French text of Laüstic.

144 pp.   0-14-044476-9 $ 8.95

W. SOMERSET MAUGHAM
1874–1965, ENGLISH

Cakes and Ale

In this novel Maugham creates the unauthorized biography of Edward Driffield, a man lionized by literary society, and whose second wife learns more about his less respectable days than she cares to know.

20TH-CENTURY CLASSICS

208 pp.   0-14-018588-7 $ 8.95

Liza of Lambeth

Maugham's first novel is about the gloomy, poverty-stricken world of South London in the 1890s and how it affects one young girl who tries to escape from it.

20TH-CENTURY CLASSICS

126 pp.   0-14-018593-3 $ 8.95

The Merry-Go-Round

An elderly spinster who takes a cool view of emotional entanglements reveals that love in the Edwardian Age involved the same intricacies that it does today.

20TH-CENTURY CLASSICS

352 pp.   0-14-018596-8 $ 9.95

Mrs. Craddock

In this penetrating study of an unequal marriage, Maugham explores the nature of love and happiness and finds that the two rarely coincide.

20TH-CENTURY CLASSICS

256 pp.   0-14-018594-1 $ 9.95

The Narrow Corner

First published in 1932, this volume recalls many of Maugham's best short stories, featuring a story of love, money, and mutiny.

20TH-CENTURY CLASSICS

224 pp.   0-14-018598-4 $ 8.95

Of Human Bondage

Introduced by Robert Calder

An obsessive love affair provides the pivot of this powerful evocation of a young man's progress to maturity in the years before the First World War.

20TH-CENTURY CLASSICS

608 pp.   0-14-018522-4 $ 9.95

The Painted Veil

Set in Hong Kong during the heart of a cholera epidemic, this novel portrays a young woman as she learns the true meaning of love—but her discovery comes too late.

20TH-CENTURY CLASSICS

256 pp.   0-14-018599-2 $ 9.95

The Razor's Edge

Introduced by Anthony Curtis

They are intimate acquaintances but less than friends who meet and part in post-war London and Paris, in this story that encompasses the pain, passion, and poignancy of life itself.

20TH-CENTURY CLASSICS

320 pp.   0-14-018523-2 $ 8.95

The Summing Up

For a description, see AUTOBIOGRAPHY AND BIOGRAPHY.

A Writer's Notebook

For a description, see AUTOBIOGRAPHY AND BIOGRAPHY.

GUY DE MAUPASSANT
1850–1893, FRENCH

Bel Ami

Translated by Douglas Parmée

In this analysis of power and its corrupting influence, de Maupassant captures the sleaziness, manipulation, and mediocrity prevalent in the elegant salons of Paris during the Belle Époque.

416 pp.   0-14-044315-0 $ 6.95

Pierre and Jean

Translated and introduced by
Leonard Tancock

An intensely personal story of suspicion, jealousy, and family love, this novel shows the influence of such masters as Zola and Flaubert on de Maupassant's writings.

176 pp.   0-14-044358-4 $ 7.95

Selected Short Stories

Translated by Roger Colet

These thirty stories, including "Boule de Suif," "Madame Tellier's Establishment," "The Jewels," "The Mask," "A Duel," and "Mother Savage" illuminate and delineate de Maupassant's art.

368 pp.   0-14-044243-X $ 8.95

A Woman's Life

Translated by H. N. P. Sloman

In this, his most popular full-length novel, de Maupassant exposes with his characteristic detachment and precision the evil around a woman misused by both her husband and her son.

208 pp.   0-14-044161-1 $ 7.95

FRANÇOIS MAURIAC
1885–1970, FRENCH

Thérèse

Translated by Gerard Hopkins

In four stories set in Bordeaux and Paris and in a world bound by conventional morality, Mauriac charts the tortured life of Thérèse Desqueyroux, who dares to act longings buried deep in her heart and whose refusal to bow to convention condemns her to solitude.

20TH-CENTURY CLASSICS

400 pp.   0-14-018153-9 $ 10.95

F. M. MAYOR
1872–1932, ENGLISH

The Rector's Daughter

The quiet life of a plain, reliable, middle-aged rector's daughter is shaken to the core by an unsolicited love affair.

20TH-CENTURY CLASSICS

224 pp.   0-14-018265-9 $ 9.95

HERMAN MELVILLE
1819–1891, AMERICAN

Billy Budd and Other Stories

Selected and introduced by
Frederick Busch

Receiving more literary success in England than from his compatriots, Melville's fortunes were as unpredictable as the sea he wrote about. The title piece was still in manuscript form when he died. Other entries include "Bartleby," "The Piazza," "The Encantadas," "The Bell-Tower," "Benito Cereno," "The Paradise of Bachelors," and "The Tartarus of Maids."

416 pp.   0-14-039053-7 $ 6.95

The Confidence-Man

Edited and introduced by
Stephen Matterson

Part satire, part allegory, part hoax, Melville explores America and American values in this metaphysical comedy.

400 pp.   0-14-044547-1 $ 8.95

Moby-Dick
Or, The Whale

Introduced by Andrew Delbanco

The epic story of whales, whaling, and the sea, and a madman's quest for deliverance, *Moby-Dick* is a primary text of American literature. This edition contains notes, an introductory essay, maps, illustrations, and a glossary.

624 pp.   0-14-039084-7 $ 9.95

Redburn

Edited by Harold Beaver

Based on his own experiences on a ship sailing between New York and Liverpool, Melville tells a powerful story of pastoral innocence transformed to disenchantment and disillusionment.

448 pp.   0-14-043105-5 $ 8.95

Typee

Edited by George Woodcock

Set in the paradise of a South Sea island, this combination of fact and fiction draws a comparison between the idyllic life of "savages" and industrial America in the nineteenth century.

368 pp.   0-14-043070-9 $ 9.95

GEORGE MEREDITH
1828–1909, ENGLISH

The Egoist

Edited by Angus Wilson

In this consummate portrait of vanity and egoism, Meredith uses comedy as the great dissolver of artifice.

608 pp.   0-14-043034-2 $ 10.95

HERMAN MELVILLE
1819–1891, American

Melville was born in New York, the son of a merchant, and largely self-educated. He started writing after having first sailed to Liverpool in 1839, where he joined the whaler *Acushnet* bound for the Pacific. Deserting ship the following year in the Marquesas, he made his way to Tahiti and Honolulu, returning as an ordinary seaman to Boston, where he was discharged in October 1844. Books based on these adventures, which include his masterpiece, *Moby-Dick*, won him immediate success. However, this literary renown soon faded; his complexity increasingly alienated readers. Melville died virtually forgotten and it was not until the 1920s that his reputation underwent the revision which has made him such a key figure in American literature.

MICHEL DE MONTAIGNE
1533–1592, FRENCH

An Apology for Raymond Sebond

For a description, see HISTORY AND
POLITICS.

The Complete Essays

*Translated and introduced by
M. A. Screech*

The essential Montaigne, this edition
includes all of his essays, giving readers
ample opportunity to relish "a meticulous translation of the *Essays* in plain
contemporary English, and with no
avoidance of those frank or obscene
terms that Montaigne was not afraid of
using" (*New York Review of Books*).

1,344 pp.   0-14-044604-4 $ 22.50

The Essays: A Selection

*Translated and introduced by
M. A. Screech*

Reflections by the creator of the essay
form display the humane, skeptical, humorous, and honest views of Montaigne, revealing his thoughts on
sexuality, religion, cannibals, intellectu-
als, and other unexpected themes.

480 pp.   0-14-044602-8 $ 9.95

CHARLES DE MONTESQUIEU
1689–1755, FRENCH

Persian Letters

Translated by C. J. Betts

In the form of letters between two Persian travelers in eighteenth-century Europe, this novel was written to show that
France was moving from benevolent
monarchy to royal tyranny.

352 pp.   0-14-044281-2 $ 7.95

WILLIAM MORRIS
1834–1896, ENGLISH

News from Nowhere and Other Writings

Edited and introduced by Clive Wilmer

Contained within one volume are the
brilliant utopian novel (1891) and other
essays by the socialist, pioneering envi-
ronmentalist, designer-craftsman
William Morris whose antipathy towards the dehumanization of the Industrial Revolution was well-known.

480 pp.   0-14-043330-9 $ 9.95

MULTATULI
1820–1887, DUTCH

Max Havelaar
Or The Coffee Auctions of the Dutch Trading Company

*Translated with notes by Roy Edwards
Introduced by R. P. Meijer*

Based on the author's actual experiences, *Max Havelaar* is one of the most
forceful indictments of colonialism ever
written. Its portrayal of colonial cruelty
is rendered in prose that ranges from
colloquial informality to cadences of
biblical resonance, and the sophistication of its satire led D. H. Lawrence to
compare it to the works of Swift, Gogol,
and Twain.

352 pp.   0-14-044516-1 $ 12.95

V. S. NAIPAUL
B. 1932, TRINIDADIAN

A House for Mr. Biswas

Introduced by Ian Buruma

Through the story of Mr. Biswas, who struggles against the forces of myth, ritual, custom, and familial obligation to own a house of his own, Naipaul offers a subtle, tragicomic analysis of the human impact of colonialism.

20TH-CENTURY CLASSICS

566 pp.   0-14-018604-2 $ 11.95

R. K. NARAYAN
B. 1906, INDIAN

The Guide

Raju used to be India's most corrupt tourist guide, but now a peasant mistakes him for a holy man. Gradually he begins to play the part—so well, in fact, that God himself intervenes to put Raju's new holiness to the test.

20TH-CENTURY CLASSICS

224 pp.   0-14-018547-X $ 10.95

Malgudi Days

In this marvelous collection of stories, all kinds of people—simple and not so simple—are drawn in full color and endearing domestic detail as the author creates the imaginary city of Malgudi.

20TH-CENTURY CLASSICS

256 pp.   0-14-018543-7 $ 9.95

The Man-Eater of Malgudi

Narayan slyly and sometimes wickedly weaves a story of comedic and vastly human conflict in the enchanted city of Malgudi—an entangling dispute between the local owner of a small printing press and his tenant, Vasu, a pugnacious taxidermist in search of an elephant for his stuffed collection.

20TH-CENTURY CLASSICS

176 pp.   0-14-018548-8 $ 7.95

The Painter of Signs

A wry, funny, bittersweet story of love getting in the way of progress, involving Raman, a sign-painter, and the thrillingly independent Daisy, who wishes to bring birth control to the city of Malgudi.

20TH-CENTURY CLASSICS

144 pp.   0-14-018549-6 $ 7.95

MICHEL DE MONTAIGNE
1533–1592, French

"Montaigne is one of the great sages of that modern world which in a sense began with the Renaissance. He is the bridge linking the thought of pagan antiquity and of Christian antiquity with our own." —**M. A. Screech**

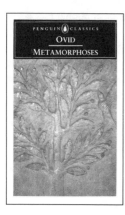

The Rāmayāna

This shortened modern prose version of the Indian epic—parts of which date from 500 B.C.—was composed by one of today's supreme storytellers.

20TH-CENTURY CLASSICS

190 pp.   0-14-018700-6 $ 8.95

Talkative Man

The arrival of a stranger on the Delhi train marks the beginning of some odd and wondrous events in the volatile life of the village of Malgudi.

20TH-CENTURY CLASSICS

128 pp.   0-14-018546-1 $ 9.95

A Tiger for Malgudi

A comic view of human absurdities told from the point of view of a tiger named Raga. One of Narayan's beloved Malgudi novels, this work is infused with Hindu mysticism and delightful humor.

20TH-CENTURY CLASSICS

160 pp.   0-14-018545-3 $ 8.95

Under the Banyan Tree

This collection of twenty-eight stories is rich in wry, warmly observed characters from every walk of Indian life, all of whose lives are a microcosm of the human experience.

20TH-CENTURY CLASSICS

208 pp.   0-14-018544-5 $ 8.95

THOMAS NASHE
1567–C. 1601, ENGLISH

The Unfortunate Traveller and Other Works

Edited and introduced by J. B. Steane

Elizabethan manners, morality, and mirth are captured in this selection from the works of Thomas Nashe—pamphleteer, poet, satirist, scholar, moralist, and jester.

512 pp.   0-14-043067-9 $ 11.95

FRANK NORRIS
1870–1902, AMERICAN

McTeague
A Story of San Francisco

Edited and introduced by Kevin Starr

Set against the harsh California landscape, this novel by one of America's foremost literary realists preserves, in almost obsessive detail, the darker side of a still young San Francisco.

20TH-CENTURY CLASSICS

496 pp.   0-14-018769-3 $ 10.95

The Octopus
A Story of California
Introduced by Kevin Starr

Based on an actual violent dispute in California's Great Central Valley, *The Octopus* (1901) depicts the clash between classic opposing interests of the Progressive era—the farmers and the land-hungry railroads that distributed their wheat.

20TH-CENTURY CLASSICS

496 pp.   0-14-018770-7 $ 10.95

The Pit
A Story of Chicago
Introduced by Joseph A. McElrath, Jr.

This classic literary critique of American turn-of-the-century capitalism reveals Frank Norris's powerful story of an obsessed trader intent on cornering the wheat market, and the consequences of his unchecked greed.

20TH-CENTURY CLASSICS

496 pp.   0-14-018758-8 $ 10.95

OVID
43 B.C.–A.D. 17, ROMAN

Metamorphoses
Translated and introduced by Mary M. Innes

Culled from Greek poems and myths, Latin folklore, and tales from Babylon and the East, Ovid's *Metamorphoses* is examined in historical and literary context in Innes's introduction.

368 pp.   0-14-044058-5 $ 7.95

The Poems of Exile
Translated and introduced by Peter Green

These poems written during his exile from Rome on charges of literary obscenity reveal Ovid's political opinions and his laments for his homeland.

560 pp.   0-14-044407-6 $ 10.95

OVID
43 B.C.–A.D. 17, Roman

Ovid was born at Sulmo in central Italy. He was sent to Rome to attend the schools of the famous rhetoricians but, realizing that his talent lay with poetry rather than politics, he began instead to cultivate the acquaintance of literary Romans. His first published work was *Amores*, a collection of short love poems; then followed *Heroides*, verse-letters supposedly written by deserted ladies to their former lovers; *Ars Amatoria,* a handbook on love; *Remedia Amoris* and *Metamorphoses*. By A.D. 8 he was a prominent literary figure in Rome but in the same year the Emperor Augustus expelled him, for some unknown offense, to Tomis on the Black Sea. He continued to write, and his account of exile's emotional upheavals, *The Poems of Exile*, rings totally true. He died, still in exile, in A.D. 17.

DOROTHY PARKER
1893–1967, AMERICAN

Collected Stories

Edited by Mikki Breese
Introduced by Regina Barreca

This collection features some of Parker's best-known stories—"Big Blonde," which won the O. Henry Prize in 1929, "A Telephone Call," a poignant depiction of a woman desperate to hear from her lover, and "The Lovely Leave," a tale of the brief, unhappy meeting of a soldier and his wife—as well as many never previously collected. 🔊

20TH-CENTURY CLASSICS
352 pp.   0-14-018939-4 $ 11.95

WALTER PATER
1839–1894, ENGLISH

Marius the Epicurean

Edited and introduced with notes by Michael Levey

This inimitable historical and autobiographical fiction, set in the Rome of Marcus Aurelius, also reflects the values of late-Victorian England.

320 pp.   0-14-043236-1 $ 10.95

THOMAS LOVE PEACOCK
1785–1866, ENGLISH

Nightmare Abbey, Crotchet Castle

Edited by Raymond Wright

Two of Peacock's wittiest works, parodies of the Gothic novel's excesses, are included here in one volume.

284 pp.   0-14-043045-8 $ 9.95

BENITO PÉREZ GALDÓS
1843–1920, SPANISH

Fortunata and Jacinta

Translated and introduced by Agnes Moncy Gullóon

Set against the political tumult of nineteenth-century Madrid, this controversial novel of love and obsession brings alive, in the tradition of Dickens and Balzac, the rich textures and traditions of time.

848 pp.   0-14-043305-8 $ 13.95

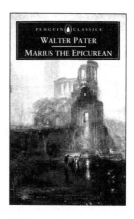

PETRONIUS and SENECA
D. A.D. 66; C. 4 B.C.–A.D. 65, ROMAN

The Satyricon, The Apocolocyntosis

Translated by J. P. Sullivan

In *The Satyricon*, the racy adventures of the impotent Encolpius and his friends and lovers provide the definitive portrait of the age of Nero. Included also in this volume is *The Apocolocyntosis*, a malicious skit on "the definition of Claudius the Clod," designed by Seneca to ingratiate himself with Claudius's successor, Nero.

256 pp.   0-14-044489-0 $ 9.95

Essays

For a description, see HISTORY AND POLITICS.

EDGAR ALLAN POE
1809–1849, AMERICAN

Comedies and Satires

Edited and introduced by David Galloway

Nineteen often neglected comedies and satires reveal the lighter side of a master of literary darkness.

256 pp.   0-14-039055-3 $ 8.95

The Fall of the House of Usher and Other Writings

Edited by David Galloway

This selection encompasses seventeen poems, including "The Raven," "Annabel Lee," and "The Bells"; nineteen tales, including "The Fall of the House of Usher," "The Murders in the Rue Morgue," "The Tell-Tale Heart," "The Masque of the Red Death," and "The Pit and the Pendulum"; and sixteen essays and reviews. ▣

544 pp.   0-14-043291-4 $ 6.95

The Narrative of Arthur Gordon Pym of Nantucket

Edited by Harold Beaver

The friendship and friction between a stowaway and the captain's son on a brig form the background for this exciting blend of romantic adventure and realistic detail; Jules Verne's ingenious sequel *Le Sphinx des Glaces* is included in this edition.

320 pp.   0-14-043097-0 $ 8.95

The Science Fiction of Edgar Allan Poe

Edited by Harold Beaver

The sixteen stories in this collection, including the celebrated "Eureka," reveal Poe as both an apocalyptic prophet and a pioneer of science fiction.

430 pp.   0-14-043106-3 $ 9.95

EDGAR ALLAN POE

1809–1849, American

Edgar Allan Poe inspired strongly divergent views of his talents. Emerson dismissed him as the "jingle man," Lowell pronounced him "three-fifths genius and two-fifths sheer fudge," and Yeats declared that he was "always and for all lands a great poet." In fact his greatest impact was felt abroad: his poetry influenced Tennyson and Swinburne; his stories inspired Stevenson, Conan Doyle, and Verne; Baudelaire wrote several essays about him and translated his works. Although Poe cared more for his poetry, he is remembered by many for his evocative Gothic tales and credited with being the creator of the modern detective story.

ABBÉ PRÉVOST
1697–1763, FRENCH

Manon Lescaut

Newly introduced by Jean Sgard
Translated by Leonard Tancock

Young Chevalier des Grieux's account discloses his love affair with Manon, a femme fatale who makes his life a torment—and without whom it is meaningless.

192 pp.   0-14-044559-5 $ 9.95

ALEXANDER PUSHKIN
1799–1837, RUSSIAN

Eugene Onegin

Introduced by Johnston Bayley
Translated by Charles Johnston

Hailed by critics as the finest English-language rendering ever achieved, Charles Johnston's new verse translation of *Eugene Onegin* captures the lyric intensity and gusto of Pushkin's incomparable poem.

240 pp.   0-14-044394-0 $ 7.95

The Queen of Spades and Other Stories

Translated and introduced by Rosemary Edmonds

Known as Russia's greatest poet, Pushkin was equally at ease working in other literary forms. Of the prose collected here, "The Captain's Daughter" chronicles the Pugachev Rebellion of 1770.

320 pp.   0-14-044119-0 $ 9.95

THOMAS PYNCHON
B. 1927, AMERICAN

Gravity's Rainbow

With the publication of this convoluted, allusive novel about a metaphysical quest, Pynchon shook the literary world and emerged as one of the greatest writers of the century.

20TH-CENTURY CLASSICS
528 pp.   0-14-018859-2 $ 15.95

QU YUAN and OTHER POETS
C. 1ST AND 2ND CENTURIES, CHINESE

The Songs of the South
An Anthology of Ancient Chinese Poems by Qu Yuan and Other Poets

For a description, see POETRY.

FRANCISCO DE QUEVEDO
1580–1645, SPANISH

Two Spanish Picaresque Novels

Translated by Michael Alpert

A vigorous and earthy humor animates these sixteenth- and seventeenth-century novels, Quevedo's *El Buscón (The Swindler)* and *Lazarillo de Tormes,* author unknown, in which a slightly disreputable hero who lives by his wits replaces the romantic hero of earlier writings.

216 pp.   0-14-044211-1 $ 9.95

Gargantua and Pantagruel

Translated by J. M. Cohen

Written by a Franciscan monk who was at the center of the sixteenth-century humanist movement, this robust epic parodies everyone from classic authors to Rabelais's own contemporaries.

720 pp.   0-14-044047-X $ 9.95

Selected Writings

*Edited and introduced by
Gerald Hammond*

This wide-ranging collection includes extensive selections from *The Discovery of Guiana*, *The Last Fight of the Revenge*, and the apocalyptic *History of the World*.

304 pp.   0-14-043257-4 $ 6.95

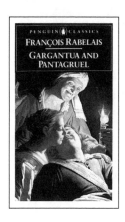

Letters 1931–1966

For a description, see AUTOBIOGRAPHY AND BIOGRAPHY.

Sleep It Off Lady

In this collection of sixteen short stories, Rhys gives voice to the alienation and loneliness of people who, somehow, have been left behind. She evokes with great sensitivity both the dignity and humiliations of lives shaped by loss—from the abrupt loss of innocence to the gradual loss of hope.

20TH-CENTURY CLASSICS

176 pp.   0-14-018345-0 $ 12.95

Smile Please
An Unfinished Autobiography

Foreword by Diana Athill

In *Smile Please*, Rhys recalls her childhood on the island of Dominica and the influences that shaped her and much of her fictional world. Diana Athill, Rhys's longtime editor, has organized these fragments with meticulous care, preserving Rhys's impeccable style and her unforgettable voice.

20TH-CENTURY CLASSICS

176 pp.   0-14-018405-8 $ 9.95

SAMUEL RICHARDSON
1689–1761, ENGLISH

Clarissa

Edited and introduced by Angus Ross

This tale of attracted lovers, one of a virtuous young woman, the other a charming and wicked young man, is, like *Pamela*, a novel told in psychologically revealing letters. Oversize format.

1,536 pp.   0-14-043215-9 $ 21.95

Pamela

Edited by Peter Sabor
Introduced by Margaret Doody

Told in a series of letters, this story of a maid pursued by her dead mistress's son features the first English heroine to work for a living and deals with such matters as the perversion of sex into power, a radical theme in 1740.

544 pp.   0-14-043140-3 $ 6.95

DAPHNE ROOKE
B. 1914, S. AFRICAN

Mittee

Introduced by J. M. Coetzee

Here is a novel that is a searing indictment of the alienation created by Afrikaaner nationalism, written by one of South Africa's finest post-war novelists.

20TH-CENTURY CLASSICS

224 pp.   0-14-018431-7 $ 9.95

SUSANNA ROWSON
1762–1824, AMERICAN

Charlotte Temple and Lucy Temple

Edited and introduced by Ann Douglas

Rowson's tale of a young girl who elopes to America only to be abandoned by her fiancé was once the bestselling novel in American literary history. This paperback edition also includes *Lucy Temple*, the fascinating story of Charlotte's orphaned daughter.

336 pp.   0-14-039080-4 $ 10.95

SAKI (H. H. MUNRO)
1870–1916, SCOTTISH

The Chronicles of Clovis

Introduced by Auberon Waugh

From the cynical to the supernatural, twenty-eight stories lay bare the brittle façade of the Edwardian upper class.

20TH-CENTURY CLASSICS

176 pp.   0-14-018349-3 $ 5.95

The Complete Saki

Introduced by Noël Coward

More than 140 short stories, novels, and plays make up this complete collection of Saki's work, and display the brilliant wit and biting sophistication of a master of social satire.

20TH-CENTURY CLASSICS

960 pp.   0-14-018420-1 $ 12.95

MIKHAIL SALTYKOV-SHCHEDRIN
1826–1889, RUSSIAN

The Golovlyov Family

Translated by Ronald Wilks
Introduced by V. S. Pritchett and Ronald Wilks

The arresting portrait of a bourgeois family in decline mirrors the spiritual and moral decay of eighteenth-century Russia in this powerful novel of grief, idleness, and ignorance.

288 pp.   0-14-044490-4 $ 6.95

OLIVE SCHREINER
1855–1920, S. AFRICAN

The Story of an African Farm

Introduced by Dan Jacobson

Written by an avid feminist and political activist and first published in 1883, this masterful novel reveals much about colonial history as it tells the story of two orphaned sisters growing up on a lonely farm in a Bible-dominated area of South Africa during the 1860s.

304 pp.   0-14-043184-5 $ 8.95

BRUNO SCHULZ
1892–1942, POLISH

The Street of Crocodiles

Translated by Celina Wieniewski
Introduced by Jerzy Ficowski

In the Polish city of Drogobych is a street of memories and dreams where recollections of Schulz's boyhood are evoked in a startling blend of the real and the fantastic.

20TH-CENTURY CLASSICS

160 pp.   0-14-018625-5 $ 10.95

SIR WALTER SCOTT
1771–1832, SCOTTISH

The Heart of Mid-Lothian

Edited and introduced by Tony Inglis

The inventor and master of the historical novel tells the story of a determined heroine's dramatic confrontation with the justice system in a trial for infanticide, mixing historical fact with folklore from the uneasy, changing world of 1730s Scotland.

848 pp.   0-14-043129-2 $ 11.95

Ivanhoe

Edited and introduced by A. N. Wilson

A stirring and exciting re-creation of the age of chivalry, alive with such legends as Richard the Lion-Hearted and Robin Hood, this is Scott's most popular novel.

624 pp.   0-14-043143-8 $ 6.95

Old Mortality

Edited by Angus Calder

The story of two sets of "cruel and bloody bigots" at war in the late seventeenth century, this is a fast-paced chronicle of a rebellious religious movement and its impact on peasant and nobleman alike.

608 pp.   0-14-043098-9 $ 6.95

Rob Roy

An adventure tale filled with brave deeds and cowardly conspiracies, noble heroes, and despicable traitors, *Rob Roy* sweeps readers into the turmoil that erupted in England and Scotland after the death of Queen Anne. Based on the real-life Rob Roy MacGregor, it explores a common theme in Scott's work: the disappearance of the heroic values of chivalry as society became more ordered and prosperous. 🎧

512 pp.   0-14-043554-9 $ 6.95

Waverley

Edited by Andrew Hook

This highly readable story of a young man involved in the Jacobite Rebellion of 1754 blends realism and romance in a classic example of Scott's "invention"—the historical novel.

608 pp.   0-14-043071-7 $ 6.95

VARLAM SHALAMOV
1906–1982, RUSSIAN

Kolyma Tales

Translated with a foreword by John Glad

Out of his seventeen years in the Siberian labor camps of Kolyma, Shalamov fashioned a fictional re-creation of a world and created this powerful collection of stories from the raw cruelty of Soviet history.

20TH-CENTURY CLASSICS

538 pp.   0-14-018695-6 $ 11.95

MARY SHELLEY
1797–1851, ENGLISH

Frankenstein

Edited and introduced by Maurice Hindle

Shelley's Gothic horror tale, written when she was nineteen for her husband and their friend Lord Byron, was an immediate bestseller in 1818. This definitive new edition contains the revised, original text. 🎧

320 pp.   0-14-043362-7 $ 5.95

SHEN FU
C. 18TH CENT., CHINESE

Six Records of a Floating Life

Translated and introduced by Leonard Pratt and Chiang Su-Hui

This autobiographical novel contains a lively depiction of the manners and mores of turn-of-the-century China.

176 pp.   0-14-044429-7 $ 8.95

PENGUIN CLASSICS
SHEN FU
SIX RECORDS OF A
FLOATING LIFE

UPTON SINCLAIR
1878–1968, AMERICAN

The Jungle

Introduced by Ronald Gottesman

Perhaps the most influential and harrowing of Sinclair's writings, this savage novel of the Chicago stockyards established its author as one of the major modern American propaganda novelists.

432 pp.   0-14-039031-6 $ 7.95

I. J. SINGER
1893–1944, POLISH

The Brothers Ashkenazi

Translated by Joseph Singer
Introduced by Irving Howe

Yiddish novelist Singer's sweeping family saga set against the rise of capitalism and the Jewish bourgeoisie in Lodz, Poland, depicts a society torn apart by the clash between traditional ways and the burgeoning appetite for the new.

20TH-CENTURY CLASSICS

448 pp.   0-14-018777-4 $ 11.95

R. C. SHERRIFF
1896–1975, ENGLISH

Journey's End

Sherriff's powerful antiwar drama, first performed in 1928 to international acclaim, portrays a group of British officers waiting in the trenches for the German attack to begin during World War I.

20TH-CENTURY CLASSICS

96 pp.   0-14-018658-1 $ 7.95

SIR PHILIP SIDNEY
1554–1586, ENGLISH

The Countess of Pembroke's Arcadia

Edited and introduced by Maurice Evans

As much a work of entertainment and wit as of instruction, *The Arcadia* affords the best insight we have into the tastes and standards of the Elizabethans, embodying the highest literary aspirations of the age.

878 pp.   0-14-043111-X $ 10.95

TOBIAS SMOLLETT
1721–1771, SCOTTISH

The Adventures of Ferdinand Count Fathom

Edited and introduced by Paul-Gabriel Bouce

The introduction of Count Fathom, one of the most despicable villains in literary history, along with Smollett's comic irony, has earned *The Adventures* (1753) a distinctive place in the annals of the eighteenth-century novel.

512 pp.   0-14-043307-4 $ 10.95

The Expedition of Humphrey Clinker

Edited by Angus Ross

Written toward the end of Smollett's life, this picaresque tour of eighteenth-century English society abounds with eccentric characters and comic adventures.

416 pp.   0-14-043021-0 $ 6.95

The Life and Adventures of Sir Launcelot Greaves

Edited and introduced by Peter Wagner

Although it was long dismissed as an imitation of Cervantes's *Don Quixote*, this novel is a glittering, inventive, and wonderfully satiric reworking of the Arthurian legends.

272 pp.   0-14-043306-6 $ 10.95

FYODOR SOLOGUB
1863–1927, RUSSIAN

The Little Demon

Translated and edited by Ronald Wilks
Introduced by Victor Erofeyev

In this brilliant and comic novel, Sologub's depiction of provincial life echoes the realistic tradition of Russian literature, but by establishing the behavior of a verifiable madman as the norm, the author mocks the noble images of the Russian people found in the great works of the nineteenth century.

20TH-CENTURY CLASSICS

320 pp.   0-14-018638-7 $ 10.95

GERTRUDE STEIN
1874–1946, AMERICAN

Three Lives

Introduced by Ann Charters

Redefining the writer's art, "The Good Anna," "The Gentle Lena," and "Melanctha" capture the sensibilities of an author and an age, in a way that continues to influence writers of this century.

20TH-CENTURY CLASSICS

320 pp.   0-14-018184-9 $ 8.95

JOHN STEINBECK
1902–1968, AMERICAN

Burning Bright

Written as a play in story form, this novel traces the story of a man ignorant of his own sterility; a wife who commits adultery to give her husband a child; the father of the child; and the outsider whose actions affect them all.

20TH-CENTURY CLASSICS

128 pp.   0-14-018742-1 $ 8.95

Cannery Row

Introduced by Susan Shillinglaw

Steinbeck's tough but loving portrait evokes the lives of Monterey's vital laboring class and their emotional triumph over the dark existence of life in Cannery Row.

20TH-CENTURY CLASSICS

224 pp.   0-14-018737-5 $ 8.95

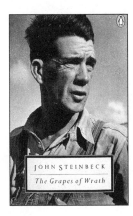

Cup of Gold

John Steinbeck's first novel, and the only historical novel he ever wrote, *Cup of Gold* brings to life the exciting, violent adventures of the infamous pirate Henry Morgan.

20TH-CENTURY CLASSICS

272 pp.   0-14-018743-X $ 9.95

East of Eden

Introduced by David Wyatt

The masterpiece of Steinbeck's later years, *East of Eden* is the powerful and vastly ambitious novel that is both family saga and a modern retelling of the book of Genesis. With a new introduction.

20TH-CENTURY CLASSICS

624 pp.   0-14-018639-5 $ 9.95

The Grapes of Wrath

Introduced by Robert DeMott

This Pulitzer Prize–winning epic of the Great Depression follows the western movement of one family and a nation in search of work and human dignity.

20TH-CENTURY CLASSICS

640 pp.   0-14-018640-9 $ 10.95

In Dubious Battle

Introduced by Warren French

This powerful social novel, set in the California apple country, is a story of labor unrest in the migrant community and the search for identity of its protagonist, young Jim Nolan.

20TH-CENTURY CLASSICS

360 pp.   0-14-018641-7 $ 9.95

The Log from the *Sea of Cortez*

Introduced by Richard Astro

This exciting day-by-day account of Steinbeck's trip to the Gulf of California with biologist Ed Ricketts, drawn from the longer *Sea of Cortez,* is a wonderful combination of science, philosophy, and high-spirited adventure.

20TH-CENTURY CLASSICS

288 pp.   0-14-018744-8 $ 9.95

The Long Valley

Introduced by John H. Timmerman

First published in 1938, this collection of stories set in the rich farmland of the Salinas Valley includes the O. Henry Prize–winning story "The Murder," as well as one of Steinbeck's most famous stories, "The Snake."

20TH-CENTURY CLASSICS

304 pp.   0-14-018745-6 $ 9.95

The Moon Is Down

Introduced by Donald V. Coers

In this masterful tale set in Norway during World War II, Steinbeck explores the effects of invasion on both the conquered and the conquerors. As he delves into the emotions of the German commander and the Norwegian traitor, and depicts the spirited patriotism of the Norwegian underground, Steinbeck uncovers profound, often unsettling truths about war—and about human nature.

20TH-CENTURY CLASSICS

192 pp.   0-14-018746-4 $ 9.95

Of Mice and Men

Introduced by Susan Shillinglaw

A parable about commitment, loneliness, hope, and loss, *Of Mice and Men* remains one of America's most widely read and beloved novels. 🖳

20TH-CENTURY CLASSICS

160 pp.   0-14-018642-5 $ 8.95

Once There Was a War

Steinbeck's dispatches filed from the front lines during World War II vividly evoke the human side of the war.

20TH-CENTURY CLASSICS

256 pp.   0-14-018747-2 $ 9.95

The Pastures of Heaven

Introduced with notes by James Nagel

Each of these interconnected tales is devoted to a family living in a fertile valley on the outskirts of Monterey, California, and the effects, either intentional or unwitting, that one family has on all of them.

20TH-CENTURY CLASSICS

256 pp.   0-14-018748-0 $ 10.95

The Pearl

Introduced by Linda Wagner-Martin

Steinbeck's tragic story introduces the diver Kino who believes that his discovery of the beautiful pearl will erase all his problems and lead his family out of poverty. His fall from innocence is one of Steinbeck's most moving and succinct fictions about American dreams. 🖳

20TH-CENTURY CLASSICS

128 pp.   0-14-018738-3 $ 8.95

The Red Pony

Introduced by John Seelye

This cycle of coming-of-age stories tells of a spirited adolescent boy whose encounters with birth and death teach him about loss and profound emptiness, instead of giving him the more conventional hero's pragmatic "maturity."

20TH-CENTURY CLASSICS

128 pp.   0-14-018739-1 $ 8.95

The Short Reign of Pippin IV

Steinbeck's only work of political satire turns the French Revolution upside down, creating the hilarious characters of the motley royal court of King Pippin.

20TH-CENTURY CLASSICS

176 pp.   0-14-018749-9 $ 9.95

To a God Unknown

Introduced by Robert DeMott

Set in familiar Steinbeck territory, *To a God Unknown* is a mystical tale, exploring one man's attempt to control the forces of nature and, ultimately, to understand the ways of God.

20TH-CENTURY CLASSICS

288 pp.   0-14-018751-0 $ 9.95

The Wayward Bus

In this imaginative and unsentimental chronicle of a bus traveling California's back roads, Steinbeck creates a vivid assortment of characters, all running away from their shattered dreams but hoping that they are running towards the promise of a future.

20TH-CENTURY CLASSICS

304 pp.   0-14-018752-9 $ 9.95

STENDHAL
1783–1842, FRENCH

The Charterhouse of Parma

Translated by C. K. Scott Moncrieff

Considered one of Stendhal's masterpieces, this fictionalized account explores the intrigues within a small Italian court during the time of Napoleon's final exile.

502 pp.   0-14-044061-5 $ 8.95

Love

Translated by Gilbert Sale and Suzanne Sale

Stendhal draws on history, literature, and his own experience in this intensely personal yet universal story of unrequited love.

336 pp.   0-14-044307-X $ 9.95

Lucien Leuwen

Translated by H. L. R. Edwards Edited by Robin Buss

Full of energy and emotion, Stendhal has created a novel of great depth and insight, re-creating the prevailing historical and social conditions.

560 pp.   0-14-044525-0 $ 8.95

Scarlet and Black

Translated by Margaret R. B. Shaw

Stendhal's greatest novel faithfully reflects the France of the decades after Waterloo.

512 pp.   0-14-044030-5 $ 5.95

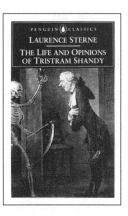

LAURENCE STERNE
1713–1768, IRISH

The Life and Opinions of Tristram Shandy

Edited by Christopher Ricks and Graham Petrie

This strange, eccentric, and complex novel about writing a novel celebrates the art of fiction with wit and genius; it remains one of the most cherished novels of the eighteenth century.

672 pp.   0-14-043019-9 $ 6.95

A Sentimental Journey

Edited by A. Alvarez and Graham Petrie

Begun as an account of a trip through France and Italy, this novel is a treasury of dramatic sketches, ironic incidents, philosophical musings, reminiscences, and anecdotes, all recorded in Sterne's delightful, meandering style.

160 pp.   0-14-043026-1 $ 4.95

ROBERT LOUIS STEVENSON
1850–1894, SCOTTISH

Dr. Jekyll and Mr. Hyde and Other Stories

Edited by Jenni Calder

This volume also includes two later stories set in the South Seas, "The Beach of Falesá" (in its unexpurgated form) and "Ebb-Tide," both of which explore the same moral terrain as Dr. Jekyll and Mr. Hyde. 🖥

304 pp.   0-14-043117-9 $ 4.95

Kidnapped

Edited and introduced by Donald McFarlan

Set in the aftermath of the Jacobite Rebellion of 1745, *Kidnapped* is a swashbuckling adventure tale of family treachery, abduction, and murder. 🖥

272 pp.   0-14-043401-1 $ 6.95

Weir of Hermiston and Other Stories

Edited and introduced by Paul Binding

In addition to Stevenson's unfinished masterpiece—a historical novel and an emotional reworking of the tensions of Stevenson's own life—this edition also includes four short stories which illustrate his progress towards Weir.

320 pp.   0-14-043138-1 $ 10.95

ROBERT LOUIS STEVENSON
1850–1894, Scottish

Robert Louis Stevenson was born in Edinburgh. The son of a prosperous civil engineer, he was expected to follow the family profession but finally was allowed to study law at Edinburgh University. Stevenson reacted violently against the Presbyterian respectability of the city's professional classes and this led to painful clashes with his parents. In his early twenties he become a professional writer. The harsh nature of the Scottish climate forced him to spend long periods abroad and he eventually settled in Samoa, where he died on December 3, 1894.

PENGUIN ● CLASSICS
BRAM STOKER
DRACULA

ADALBERT STIFTER
1805–1868, AUSTRIAN

Brigitta and Other Tales

*Translated and introduced by
Helen Watanabe-O'Kelly*

In four stories—*Brigitta, Abdias, Limestone,* and *The Forest Path*—written in the middle of the nineteenth century, the Austrian writer Adalbert Stifter created fiction whose measured prose coexists with a highly modern sensibility to the diseased subconscious and reveals the subterranean connections between our earliest experiences and our future selves.

256 pp.   0-14-044630-3 $ 10.95

BRAM STOKER
1847–1912, IRISH

Dracula

Edited and introduced by Maurice Hindle

The first—and still the most chilling—portrait of the unbridled lusts and desires of a vampire proves that Bram Stoker's *Dracula* is the ultimate terror myth. 🖸

560 pp.   0-14-043406-2 $ 9.95

HARRIET BEECHER STOWE
1811–1896, AMERICAN

Uncle Tom's Cabin
Or, Life Among the Lowly

Edited and introduced by Ann Douglas

Perhaps the most powerful document in the history of American slavery, this controversial novel prompted thousands of readers to take a stand on the issue of abolition and played a major political and social role in the Civil War period.

640 pp.   0-14-039003-0 $ 7.95

GOTTFRIED VON STRASSBURG
C. 12TH–13TH CENT., GERMAN

Tristan

Translated by A. T. Hatto

This medieval version of the legendary romance between Tristan and Isolde portrays Tristan as a sophisticated pre-Renaissance man.

384 pp.   0-14-044098-4 $ 8.95

AUGUST STRINDBERG
1849–1912, SWEDEN

By the Open Sea

*Translated and introduced by
Mary Sandbach*

Suspicion, frustration, isolation, and insanity plague an intellectual, hypersensitive bureaucrat in this novel set in Stockholm's fishing industry.

208 pp.   0-14-044488-2 $ 8.95

Inferno, From an Occult Diary

Translated and introduced by
Mary Sandbach

Inferno is an intensely powerful record of Strindberg's mental collapse; *From an Occult Diary* recounts his obsessive, un-requited love for his third wife.

448 pp.   0-14-044364-9 $ 9.95

JONATHAN SWIFT
1667–1745, ENGLISH

Gulliver's Travels

Edited by Peter Dixon and John Chalker
Introduced by Michael Foot

Swift's satirical account of Gulliver's visits to Lilliput and Brobdingnag has amused and provoked readers since it was first published in 1726; a profound comment on the Age of Reason, it is perhaps the finest satire in the English language.

368 pp.   0-14-043022-9 $ 4.95

J. M. SYNGE
1871–1909, IRISH

The Aran Islands

For a description, see TRAVEL.

RABINDRANATH TAGORE
1861–1941, INDIAN

Selected Short Stories

Translated and introduced by
William Radice

This collection of stories by India's foremost Romantic poet stands as a vivid portrait of Bengali life and landscapes.

20TH-CENTURY CLASSICS

336 pp.   0-14-018425-2 $ 9.95

WILLIAM MAKEPEACE THACKERAY
1811–1863, ENGLISH

The History of Henry Esmond

Edited by John Sutherland and
Michael Greenfield

This blend of psychological drama, romance, and history is set during the reign of Queen Anne and examines the conflicts between England's Tory-Catholic past and its Whiggish-Protestant future.

544 pp.   0-14-043049-0 $ 7.95

The History of Pendennis

Edited by Donald Hawes
Introduced by J. I. M. Stewart

This novel of a young man's passage from miserable schoolboy to striving journalist, from carefree Oxbridge to the high (and low) life of London, mirrors Thackeray's own.

814 pp.   0-14-043076-8 $ 6.95

Vanity Fair

Edited by J. I. M. Stewart

Becky Sharp, one of the most resourceful, engaging, and amoral women in literature, is the heroine of this sparkling and satirical panorama of English society during the Napoleonic Wars.

816 pp.   0-14-043035-0 $ 6.95

HENRY DAVID THOREAU
1817–1862, AMERICAN

A Year in Thoreau's Journal
Edited and introduced by H. Daniel Peck

Thoreau's journal of 1851 reveals profound ideas and observations-in-the-making, including wonderful writing on the natural history of Concord.

464 pp.   0-14-039085-5 $ 11.95

LEO TOLSTOY
1828–1910, RUSSIAN

Anna Karenin
Translated and introduced by Rosemary Edmonds

Tolstoy's intense imaginative insight is brilliantly apparent in this psychological novel and its portraits of the passionate Anna, Count Vronsky, and Levin, who may be seen as a reflection of Tolstoy himself.

865 pp.   0-14-044041-0 $ 6.95

Childhood, Boyhood, Youth
Translated by Rosemary Edmonds

These sketches, a mixture of fact and fiction, provide an expressive self-portrait of the young Tolstoy and hints of the man and writer he would become.

320 pp.   0-14-044139-5 $ 8.95

A Confession and Other Religious Writings
Translated by Jane Kentish

Tolstoy's passionate and iconoclastic writings—on issues of faith, immortality, freedom, violence, and morality—reflect his intellectual search for truth and a religion firmly grounded in reality. The selection includes: "My Confession," "Religion and Morality," "What Is Religion, and Of What Does Its Essence Consist?" and "The Law of Love and the Law of Violence."

240 pp.   0-14-044473-4 $ 9.95

The Death of Ivan Ilyich and Other Stories
Translated by Rosemary Edmonds

"The Death of Ivan Ilyich" is a magnificent story of a spiritual awakening; "The Cossacks" tells of a disenchanted nobleman who finds happiness amid the simple people of the Caucasus; "Happily Ever After" traces the maturing of romantic love into "family attachment."

336 pp.   0-14-044508-0 $ 7.95

LEO TOLSTOY
1828–1910, Russian

"All over Europe, where the futility of war and nationalism, and Capitalism and Socialism and greed and violence, is never more in evidence, men and women are continuing to ask themselves what men live by; if we shall simply continue to destroy ourselves with all the very efficient means at our disposal. This is a good time to have retranslated Tolstoy's stories: they all seem as fresh and strong and relevant to our condition as they must have done to his contemporaries." —A. N. Wilson

How Much Land Does a Man Need? and Other Stories

Edited and introduced by A. N. Wilson

These short works, ranging from Tolstoy's earliest tales to the brilliant title story, are rich in the insights and passion that characterize all of his explorations in love, war, courage, and civilization.

240 pp.   0-14-044506-4 $ 9.95

The Kreutzer Sonata and Other Stories

Translated and introduced by David McDuff

These four tales—the title story plus "The Devil," "The Forged Coupon," and "After the Ball"—embody the moral, religious, and existential themes of Tolstoy's final creative period.

288 pp.   0-14-044469-6 $ 8.95

Master and Man and Other Stories

Translated by Paul Foote

Written in the 1890s, both "Master and Man" and "Father Sergius" are preoccupied with material desires—for the flesh in one instance, and for money in the other; in "Hadji Murat," Tolstoy offers a precisely written and memorable portrait of a treacherous soldier.

272 pp.   0-14-044331-2 $ 9.95

Resurrection

Translated by Vera Traill

In this story of a fallen man and an emphatically non-Christian "resurrection," Tolstoy writes a compelling tale of the underworld and turns a highly critical eye on the law, the penal system, and the Church.

576 pp.   0-14-044184-0 $ 8.95

The Sebastopol Sketches

Translated by David McDuff

These three short stories stem from Tolstoy's military experience during the Crimean War: "Sebastopol in December," "Sebastopol in May," and "Sebastopol in August 1855."

176 pp.   0-14-044468-8 $ 8.95

War and Peace

Translated by Rosemary Edmonds

This epic presents a complete tableau of Russian society during the great Napoleonic Wars, from 1805 to 1815.

1,454 pp.   0-14-044417-3 $ 10.95

THOMAS TRAHERNE
1637–1674, ENGLISH

Selected Poems and Prose

Edited with a preface by Alan Bradford

In poems from the Dobell folio and selections from his prose masterpiece, *Centuries of Meditations,* Traherne explores the boundless potential of the human mind and spirit as he celebrates the wonder and simplicity of the child.

416 pp.   0-14-044543-9 $ 11.95

ANTHONY TROLLOPE
1815–1882, ENGLISH

Barchester Towers

Edited by Robin Gilmour
Introduced by J. K. Galbraith

In this, the second novel of the Chronicles of Barsetshire, Trollope continues the story begun in *The Warden* and explores the conflict between the High and Low Church during the mid-Victorian period.

576 pp.   0-14-043203-5 $ 5.95

Can You Forgive Her?

Edited by Stephen Wail

The first of Trollope's Palliser novels is concerned with a spirited young woman in London who rejects her faultless fiancé to marry an aggressive opportunist, a decision her Victorian society cannot accept.

848 pp.   0-14-043086-5 $ 7.95

Dr. Thorne

Edited and introduced by Ruth Rendell

One of Trollope's liveliest novels tells the story of Frank Greshman and Mary Thorne, who are intent on marriage despite Mary's ostensible poverty.

592 pp.   0-14-043326-0 $ 8.95

The Eustace Diamonds

Edited by Stephen Gillers and John Sutherland

Trollope examines the many guises of "truth" in this taut novel about Lizzie Eustace, a brave, beautiful, and unscrupulous young woman.

760 pp.   0-14-043041-5 $ 8.95

Framley Parsonage

Edited and introduced by David Skilton and Peter Miles

In the fourth of the Barsetshire Chronicles, a young Victorian clergyman's social ambition leads him to the brink of ruin.

516 pp.   0-14-043213-2 $ 8.95

The Last Chronicle of Barset

Edited by Peter Fairclough
Introduced by Laurence Lerner

In this, the last of the Barsetshire novels, Trollope draws a moving portrait of a curate who, falsely accused of theft, suffers bitter humiliation.

872 pp.   0-14-043024-5 $ 7.95

North America

Edited by Robert Mason
Introduced by John William Ward

Trollope's sympathetic interpretation of the American culture and character, and his analysis of the noble cause of saving the Union, was published following his visit to the United States during the Civil War.

240 pp.   0-14-043038-5 $ 11.95

ANTHONY TROLLOPE

1815–1882, English

"Anthony Trollope wrote about conscience and conflict, self-deception and love. Plot was subordinate to character and action to moral debate. Party politics and hunting he enjoyed, so he wrote about these too, but human relationships were what interested him, and when he explored them he was not of his Victorian age but for all time. His people are recognizably real today and if English men and women no longer talk as his people talk, some intuition tells us that their speech was once precisely as Trollope renders it. His novels are psychological studies and though much event and substance are absent, they remain exciting because their subject is the hearts and minds of human beings."—**Ruth Rendell**

Phineas Finn

Edited by John Sutherland

The second of Trollope's Palliser novels tells of the career of a hot-blooded middle-class politician whose sexual energies bring him much success with women.

752 pp.   0-14-043085-7 $ 6.95

The Small House at Allington

*Edited and introduced by
Julian Thompson*

This story of Lily Dale and her love for the ambitious, self-seeking, faithless Crosbie also offers a vivid portrayal of the social and political changes occurring in the mid-nineteenth century.

752 pp.   0-14-043325-2 $ 7.95

The Warden

Edited and introduced by Robin Gilmour

The first book in the Chronicles of Barsetshire tells the story of an elderly clergyman who resigns his church sinecure when it becomes the center of public controversy.

240 pp.   0-14-043214-0 $ 4.95

The Way We Live Now

First published in 1875 and widely regarded as the finest of all Trollope's novels, *The Way We Live Now*, satirizes to devastating effect the grip of the monetary ethic on politics, the aristocracy, the literary world, the London scene, and the marriage market. Readers will appreciate the novel's enduring resonance in the world we live in now.

816 pp.   0-14-043392-9 $ 10.95

IVAN TURGENEV
1818–1883, RUSSIAN

Fathers and Sons

Translated by Rosemary Edmonds

This powerful novel resounds with a recognition of the universal clash between generations, in this instance localized in the hostility between the reactionary 1840s and the revolutionary 1860s. With the Romanes Lecture "Fathers and Children" by Isaiah Berlin.

296 pp.   0-14-044147-6 $ 6.95

First Love

*Translated by Isaiah Berlin
Introduced by V. S. Pritchett*

Isaiah Berlin's translation reproduces in finely wrought English the original story's simplicity, lyricism, and sensitivity.

112 pp.   0-14-044335-5 $ 6.95

Home of the Gentry

Translated by Richard Freeborn

Through the story of one man, Turgenev describes a whole generation of Russians who discover the emptiness of European ideas and long for a reconciliation with their homeland.

208 pp.   0-14-044224-3 $ 8.95

On the Eve

Translated by Gilbert Gardiner

A love story with a tragic ending, this novel portrays the everyday life in a Russian country estate during the mid-nineteenth century.

240 pp.   0-14-044009-7 $ 8.95

Rudin

Translated by Richard Freeborn

Rudin, the hero of Turgenev's first novel, is in part an example of the banality of the Russian intelligentsia of the 1840s, in part a hero with the charms and failings of Don Quixote.

192 pp.   0-14-044304-5 $ 9.95

Sketches from a Hunter's Album

Translated by Richard Freeborn

First published in 1852, Turgenev's impressions of Russian peasant life and the tyranny of serfdom led to his arrest and confinement.

416 pp.   0-14-044522-6 $ 8.95

Spring Torrents

Translated and introduced by Leonard Shapiro

This is an exquisitely written, partly autobiographical treatment of one of Turgenev's favorite themes—man's inability to learn about love without first losing his innocence.

240 pp.   0-14-044369-X $ 8.95

MARK TWAIN
1835–1910, AMERICAN

The Adventures of Huckleberry Finn

Introduced by John Seelye and Peter Coveney

A novel of immeasurable richness, filled with adventures, ironies, and wonderfully drawn characters, all conveyed with Twain's mastery of humor and language, *Huckleberry Finn* is often regarded as the masterpiece of American literature.

384 pp.   0-14-039046-4 $ 4.95

MARK TWAIN
1835–1910, American

Although at times his personal life and fortune suffered severe setbacks—he was devastated by the deaths of his wife and two daughters and financially ruined for a time by failed publishing and printing ventures—Mark Twain was one of the few American writers of his time to achieve both a flourishing international reputation and a flourishing income during his lifetime. As well-known for his white suits and his mane of white hair as for his literary creations, Twain could always be counted on for a quotable comment with which he mercilessly castigated hypocrisy, imperialism, or injustice.

The Adventures of Tom Sawyer

Introduced by John Seelye

Evoking life in a small Mississippi River town, *Tom Sawyer* is Twain's hymn to the secure and fantastic world of boyhood and adventure.

256 pp.   0-14-039083-9 $ 5.95

A Connecticut Yankee in King Arthur's Court

Edited by Justin Kaplan

This imaginary confrontation of a nineteenth-century American with life in sixth-century England is both a rich, extravagant comedy and an apocalyptic vision of terrifying violence and destruction.

416 pp.   0-14-043064-4 $ 4.95

Life on the Mississippi

Introduced by James M. Cox

Twain's firsthand portrait of the steamboat age and the science of riverboat piloting recalls the history of the Mississippi River, from its discovery to the writer's own day.

464 pp.   0-14-039050-2 $ 6.95

Pudd'nhead Wilson

Edited by Malcolm Bradbury

While it retains the comic exuberance of *Huckleberry Finn,* this is Twain's darker and more disturbing account of human nature under slavery.

320 pp.   0-14-043040-7 $ 6.95

Roughing It

Edited and introduced by Hamlin Hill

A fascinating picture of the American Frontier emerges from Mark Twain's fictionalized recollections of his experiences prospecting for gold, speculating in timber, and writing for a succession of small Western newspapers during the 1860s.

592 pp.   0-14-039010-3 $ 7.95

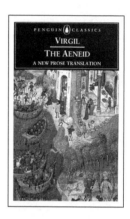

Tales, Speeches, Essays, and Sketches

Edited wnd introduced by Tom Quirk

Masterful short fiction and prose pieces display the variety of Twain's imaginative invention, his diverse talents, and his extraordinary emotional range. The volume includes the nostalgic "Early Days," the anti-imperialist "United States of Lyncherdom," fables, stories, speeches.

448 pp.   0-14-043417-8 $ 10.95

VIRGIL
70 B.C.–19 B.C., ROMAN

The Aeneid

Translated by W. F. Jackson Knight

In this fresh prose translation, W. F. Jackson Knight discusses *The Aeneid*'s impact on Western civilization, and provides a list of variations from the Oxford text.

368 pp.   0-14-044051-8 $ 8.95

The Aeneid

Translated and introduced by David West

Inspired by Homer, and inspiration for Dante and Milton, *The Aeneid* is an immortal poem describing Rome's legendary origin. This new prose translation by David West has been widely acclaimed for its directness and clarity. 🖭

288 pp.   0-14-044457-2 $ 8.95

VISNU SARMA
C. 6TH CENT., INDIAN

The Pancatantra

Translated and introduced by Chandra Rajan

This translation by a noted Sanskrit scholar of *The Pancatantra*, a book written before A.D. 570 as a manual for the ethical instruction of young princes, combines verse and prose in a highly readable version that remains faithful to the original work.

512 pp.   0-14-044596-X $ 12.95

VOLTAIRE
1694–1778, FRENCH

Candide

Translated by John Butt

Voltaire takes Candide and Dr. Pangloss through a variety of ludicrous adventures and reversals of fortune in this satirical challenge to the empty optimism prevalent in Voltaire's eighteenth-century society.

144 pp.   0-14-044004-6 $ 4.95

VIRGIL
70 B.C.–19 B.C., Roman

Roman poets imitated the Greeks in pastoral, didactic, and epic, but Virgil knew that it was easier to steal the club from Hercules than steal a line from Homer. Everything Virgil touched he charged with his own live poetic command. In later European literature the nymphs and shepherds sing to Virgil's pipe and Milton's angels fall to Virgil's orchestra. *The Eclogues, The Georgics,* and *The Aeneid* have always inspired—and will continue to inspire—generations of poets and readers.

Zadig, L'Ingénu

Translated, edited, and introduced by
John Butt

One of Voltaire's earliest tales, *Zadig* is set in the exotic East and is told in the comic spirit of Candide; *L'Ingénu*, written after *Candide*, is a darker tale in which an American Indian records his impressions of France.

192 pp.   0-14-044126-3 $ 8.95

JAKOB WASSERMAN
1873–1934, GERMAN

Caspar Hauser

Translated and introduced by
Michael Hulse

Based on a mysterious true story, this superb novel tells of the shocking fate of a young man who is cast into life among human society after a lifetime imprisonment.

20TH-CENTURY CLASSICS
416 pp.   0-14-018195-4 $ 11.95

JIŘÍ WEIL
1909–1959, CZECH

Life with a Star

Translated by Rita Klímová with
Roslyn Schloss
Preface by Philip Roth

In his preface, Philip Roth says: "This book is, without a doubt, one of the outstanding novels I've read about the fate of a Jew under the Nazis. I don't know of another like it."

20TH-CENTURY CLASSICS
224 pp.   0-14-018766-9 $ 10.95

H. G. WELLS
1866–1946, ENGLISH

Selected Short Stories

Twenty-one of Wells's stories, including "The Time Machine" and "The Truth About Pycraft," are here, presenting both his hopeful and his terrifying visions of the future.
(The Time Machine)

20TH-CENTURY CLASSICS
352 pp.   0-14-018188-1 $ 8.95

EDITH WHARTON
1862–1937, AMERICAN

The Custom of the Country

Introduced by Anita Brookner

Wharton's 1913 classic blends sharp cultural criticism with a biting indictment of American culture in a portrait of a woman advancing herself through matrimony in a world where no business transaction is honest, and no marriage is for love.

20TH-CENTURY CLASSICS
352 pp.   0-14-018190-3 $ 9.95

Ethan Frome

Introduced by Doris Grumbach

This classic novel of despair, forbidden emotion, and sexual undercurrents set against an austere New England background is different in both theme and tone from Wharton's other writings.

20TH-CENTURY CLASSICS

224 pp.   0-14-018736-7 $ 7.95

The House of Mirth

*Introduced with notes by
Cynthia Griffin Wolff*

Published in 1905, this daring novel about the shallow, brutal world of Eastern monied society deals with powerful social and feminist themes.

20TH-CENTURY CLASSICS

384 pp.   0-14-018729-4 $ 7.95

The Reef

Introduced by Anita Brookner

In this tale that explores the delicate nature of the human condition, young widow Anna Leath hires as a governess a woman whose arrival unleashes suspicions and exposes secrets that threaten to destroy Anna's carefully ordered world.

20TH-CENTURY CLASSICS

368 pp.   0-14-018731-6 $ 9.95

Summer

Introduced by Elizabeth Ammons

The novel Wharton called her "hot Ethan" is also set in the Massachusetts Berkshires and delves into the thwarted dreams and sexual passions of a repressed rural woman.

20TH-CENTURY CLASSICS

224 pp.   0-14-018679-4 $ 9.95

EDITH WHARTON

1862–1937, American

Edith Wharton was born into a prosperous social circle that centered in New York, New England, and Europe. In *The House of Mirth* (1905) and *The Age of Innocence* (1920) she brought to life ironic portraits of aristocratic American society and the constraints it placed upon women with its demands and expectations. Her 1911 tale, *Ethan Frome*, the story of the stifled existence of a snowbound, desolate household, is set in the stark New England landscape that she knew well. After her unhappy marriage had dissolved, Wharton sold "The Mount," her lavish home in western Massachusetts, and moved to France, where she lived independently, and traveled and wrote inexhaustibly, forming friendships with such notables as Henry James and Bernard Berenson.

The Aunt's Story

White's early novel portrays the confusion and alienation of heroine Theodora Goodman, who has lost her grasp on the distinction between reality and illusion while journeying back home to Australia.

20TH-CENTURY CLASSICS
288 pp.   0-14-018653-0 $ 10.95

The Cockatoos

In this collection of six short novels and several stories, Australia's masterful writer brilliantly displays his ability to see into the profound meaning of ordinary events.

20TH-CENTURY CLASSICS
288 pp.   0-14-018582-8 $ 10.95

The Eye of the Storm

One of his mature masterpieces, this is the monumental exploration of family relations, marked with longing and hatred, disappointment and love, in a story that unfolds in the room of a dying woman.

20TH-CENTURY CLASSICS
592 pp.   0-14-018605-0 $ 11.95

A Fringe of Leaves

White's brilliant novel tells of a woman shipwrecked in Australia in 1836, who discovers the sensual freedom of life among her aborigine captors.

20TH-CENTURY CLASSICS
368 pp.   0-14-018610-7 $ 10.95

The Living and the Dead

White's second novel, set in 1930s London, is an exploration of the complex web of a family's relationships and of the dilemma of whether to plunge into life or hover on its edge.

20TH-CENTURY CLASSICS
368 pp.   0-14-018526-7 $ 10.95

Riders in the Chariot

Three misfits—a mad woman, a half-caste aborigine, and a Jewish refugee—come together in the Australian wilderness to forge a new world vision.

20TH-CENTURY CLASSICS
496 pp.   0-14-018634-4 $ 11.95

The Solid Mandala

In this vibrant novel, Nobel Prize–winner (1973) White draws a touching portrait of twin brothers, one a competent man of reason, the other an innocent, loving and outgoing in a blundering way.

20TH-CENTURY CLASSICS

320 pp.   0-14-018633-6 $ 11.95

The Tree of Man

Stan Parker and his new wife, Amy, try to establish a home on a scrubby patch of land, but the Australian hillside will not cooperate, and neither will their domestic world.

20TH-CENTURY CLASSICS

480 pp.   0-14-018584-4 $ 11.95

The Twyborn Affair

Nobel Laureate Patrick White's astonishing, rich story of a man with three identities, *The Twyborn Affair* probes into the eternal ambiguities of male and female sexuality.

20TH-CENTURY CLASSICS

432 pp.   0-14-018606-9 $ 11.95

The Vivisector

An unnerving portrait of the artist as a moral monster, *The Vivisector* is the story of Hurtle Duffield, who makes art by dissecting the weaknesses of the people who love him.

20TH-CENTURY CLASSICS

1,624 pp.   0-14-018527-5 $ 11.95

Voss

Set in nineteenth-century Australia, *Voss* is the adventure epic of an explorer and the young woman with whom he shares a secret obsessive passion.

20TH-CENTURY CLASSICS

448 pp.   0-14-018623-9 $ 11.95

OSCAR WILDE
1854–1900, IRISH

Complete Short Fiction

Edited and introduced by Ian Small

This volume gathers together the short masterpieces that brought Wilde his first fame as a writer of fiction, and includes the complete texts of *The Happy Prince and Other Tales*; *A House of Pomegranates*; *Lord Arthur Savile's Crime and Other Stories*; six "Poems in Prose," and "Portrait of Mr. W. H."

336 pp.   0-14-043423-2 $ 9.95

De Profundis and Other Writings

Edited by Hesketh Pearson

Caught up in a colorful life interspersed with literary success, Wilde's tempestuous style eventually led to a circumstance of which the title piece is the result. Also featured are "The Soul of Man Under Socialism," "The Decay of Lying," and a selection of poems, including "Sonnet to Liberty," "Requiescat," and "To My Wife."

256 pp.   0-14-043089-X $ 7.95

The Picture of Dorian Gray

Edited and introduced by Peter Ackroyd

First published to scandal and protest in 1890, Oscar Wilde's story of a flamboyant hedonist is a sterling example of Wilde's wit and aestheticism.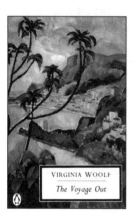

272 pp.   0-14-043187-X $ 5.95

JOHN WILMOT, EARL OF ROCHESTER
1647–1680, ENGLISH

The Complete Works

Edited and introduced by Frank H. Ellis

This volume encompasses the works of Rochester, the Restoration's infamous literary rake, hedonist, and master of satire—tragic verse, prose comedy, boisterous songs, rich rhymes and language, and frank explorations of sexual matters.

464 pp.   0-14-042362-1 $ 11.95

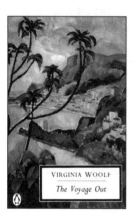

VIRGINIA WOOLF
The Voyage Out

OWEN WISTER
1860–1938, AMERICAN

The Virginian

Introduced by John Seelye

Owen Wister's powerful story of the tall, silent stranger who rides into an uncivilized West and defeats the forces of evil introduces a figure that became an enduring part of American mythology.

512 pp.   0-14-039065-0 $ 8.95

MARY WOLLSTONECRAFT and MARY SHELLEY
1759–1797, ENGLISH
1797–1851, ENGLISH

Mary/Maria/Matilda

Edited and introduced by Janet Todd

Three short novels written by mother and daughter offer insight into the personal lives of both authors as they illuminate struggles for identity within the early feminist movement; *Matilda* explores the incestuous relationship of a father and daughter.

256 pp.   0-14-043371-6 $ 10.95

VIRGINIA WOOLF
1882–1941, ENGLISH

The Voyage Out

Woolf's first novel is the story of an impressionable young Englishwoman sailing to South America, whose innocence makes her susceptible to love and ripe for tragedy.

20TH-CENTURY CLASSICS
432 pp.   0-14-018563-1 $ 9.95

WILLIAM WORDSWORTH
1771–1855, ENGLISH

Selected Prose Writings

Edited and introduced by
John O. Hayden

Twenty thematically arranged essays, letters, and prose pieces display the poet's far-reaching interests in politics, social concerns, aesthetics, and literary theory.

528 pp.   0-14-043292-2 $ 10.95

YEVGENY ZAMYATIN
1884–1937, RUSSIAN

We

Translated and introduced by
Clarence Brown

This dystopian novel was suppressed in Russia for more than sixty years but has long been recognized as the archetypal modern fiction of the totalitarian future—and the inspiration for George Orwell's *1984*.

20TH-CENTURY CLASSICS

240 pp.   0-14-018585-2 $ 10.95

ÉMILE ZOLA
1840–1902, FRENCH

The Debacle

Translated by Leonard Tancock

Zola's only purely historical work, this realistic, detailed, and accurate account of France's defeat in the Franco-Prussian War is a grim testament to the human horrors of war.

510 pp.   0-14-044280-4 $ 9.95

The Earth

Translated and introduced by
Douglas Parmée

With humor and flashes of tenderness, Zola depicts the human cycle of birth, marriage, and death against the natural changes of the agricultural seasons.

512 pp.   0-14-044387-8 $ 7.95

Germinal

Translated and introduced by
Leonard Tancock

Written by Zola to draw attention to the misery prevailing among the lower class in France during the Second Empire, *Germinal* depicts the grim struggle between capital and labor in a coalfield in northern France.

512 pp.   0-14-044045-3 $ 5.95

La Bête Humaine

Translated by Leonard Tancock

In this taut thriller of violent passions, crime, and the law, Zola bitterly attacks the politics and corruption of the French judicial system.

368 pp.   0-14-044327-4 $ 9.95

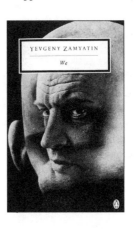

L'Assommoir

Translated by Leonard Tancock

A potent example of naturalist writing, which Zola fiercely advocated, this attempt is one of the first "classical tragedies" to detail working-class existence in the slums of a great city.

424 pp.   0-14-044231-6 $ 6.95

Nana

Translated by George Holden

An evocation of the corrupt world of the Second Empire, this story of a prostitute embodies Zola's theory that behavior is predetermined by one's origin.

470 pp.   0-14-044263-4 $ 6.95

Thérèse Raquin

Translated by Leonard Tancock

This tale of adultery, murder, and revenge, condemned as pornography when it was published in 1868, is one of Zola's earliest novels.

265 pp.   0-14-044120-4 $ 8.95

PHILOSOPHY

Early Greek Philosophy

Translated and introduced by Jonathan Barnes

The earliest Western philosophers, the pre-Socratics, are profiled in this comprehensive volume, which includes a general introduction and a synopsis of their historical and ideological development, as well as brief introductions to each philosopher's work.

320 pp.   0-14-044461-0 $ 9.95

The Laws of Manu

Translated by Wendy Doniger and Brian K. Smith

No understanding of modern India is possible without this extraordinary model of jurisprudence, philosophy, and religion, written from 200 B.C. to A.D. 200.

368 pp.   0-14-044540-4 $ 10.95

Mencius

Translated and introduced by D. C. Lau

The fullest of the four great Confucian texts, *Mencius* draws out the implications of the master's moral principles and reinterprets them for survival in the harsh conditions of the fourth century B.C., stressing the importance of individual conscience and the necessity for morality in personal and public life.

288 pp.   0-14-044228-6 $ 9.95

HANNAH ARENDT
1906–1975, GERMAN

Between Past and Future

Arendt's penetrating analysis of the complex crises of meaning in modern society and political philosophy is presented with her impassioned exercises for guiding readers toward the reinvigoration of the concepts of justice, reason, responsibility, virtue, and glory.

20TH-CENTURY CLASSICS

320 pp.   0-14-018650-6 $ 11.95

ARISTOTLE
384 B.C.–322 B.C., GREEK

The Art of Rhetoric

*Translated and introduced by
Hugh Lawson-Tancred*

With this book, Aristotle establishes the methods of informal reasoning, providing the first aesthetic evaluation of prose style and detailed observations of character and emotions.

304 pp.   0-14-044510-2 $ 9.95

The Athenian Constitution

*Translated and introduced by
P. J. Rhodes*

This is the single most important extant source for the study of the institutions of classical Athens. "Clearly and accurately translated.... Lucid introduction and notes, and excellent analytical summaries, introduce each chapter."
—S. M. Burstein, California State University, Los Angeles

208 pp.   0-14-044431-9 $ 8.95

De Anima

*Translated and introduced by
Hugh Lawson-Tancred*

Considering the nature of life, Aristotle surveys and rejects the ideas of Plato and the pre-Socratics, developing his philosophy of the soul and mind, and introducing the central concepts of form and matter to explain perception, thought, and motivation.

256 pp.   0-14-044471-8 $ 8.95

Ethics

Translated by J. A. K. Thomson

In a work which had tremendous impact on Western moral philosophy, Aristotle treats ethics as a practical rather than a theoretical science, and introduces psychology into the study of human behavior.

384 pp.   0-14-044055-0 $ 9.95

The Politics

*Translated and introduced by
T. A. Sinclair
Revised and re-presented by
Trevor J. Saunders*

The search for the ideal state and the best possible constitution is the basis for the last great work of Greek political thought.

512 pp.   0-14-044421-1 $ 9.95

MARCUS AURELIUS
121–180, ROMAN

Meditations

Translated and introduced by Maxwell Staniforth

These musings, maxims, and thoughts on life and death reflect the Roman emperor's adherence to the Stoic philosophy.

192 pp.   0-14-044140-9 $ 8.95

FRANCIS BACON
1561–1626, ENGLISH

The Essays

Edited and introduced by John Pitcher

Including the fifty-eight essays of the 1625 edition, this collection comprises reflections on the successful conduct of life and management of men, as well as reworkings of many of the ideas of Bacon's philosophical and scientific writings.

288 pp.   0-14-043216-7 $ 9.95

GEORGE BERKELEY
1685–1753, IRISH

Principles of Human Knowledge and Three Dialogues Between Hylas and Philonius

Edited and introduced by Roger Woolhouse

These two masterpieces of empirical thought elucidate Berkeley's theories. The extensive introduction offers biographical and historical background and traces Berkeley's influence on modern philosophers.

224 pp.   0-14-043293-0 $ 8.95

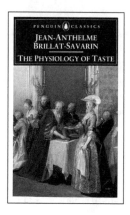

ANCIUS BOETHIUS
480–524, ROMAN

The Consolation of Philosophy

Translated and introduced by V. E. Watts

This influential book mingles verse and prose in a sacred dialogue reflecting the doctrines of Plato, Aristotle, the Stoics, and the Neoplatonists.

192 pp.   0-14-044208-1 $ 9.95

JEAN–ANTHELME BRILLAT-SAVARIN
1755–1826, FRENCH

The Physiology of Taste

Translated and introduced by Anne Drayton

First published in 1825, this book is a brilliant treatise on the pleasures of eating and the rich arts of food, wine, and philosophy, written by a famed French gastronome. Recipes are included.

384 pp.   0-14-044614-1 $ 12.95

The Major Works

Edited and introduced by C. A. Patrides

The English author and physician Sir Thomas Browne encapsulates seventeenth-century social, religious, and intellectual concerns.

560 pp.   0-14-043109-8 $ 9.95

Selected Writings

Edited by Alan Shelston

This representative selection from Carlyle's writings includes the complete *Chartism*, as well as chapters from *Sartor Resartus*, *The French Revolution*, *On Heroes*, and the *History of ... Frederick the Great*.

400 pp.   0-14-043065-2 $ 10.95

The Nature of the Gods

Introduced by J. M. Ross
Translated by H. C. P. McGregor

In *De Natura Deorum*, Cicero sets out the ancient Greeks' conclusions about the existence and nature of deities and the extent of their involvement in human affairs.

280 pp.   0-14-044265-0 $ 8.95

On the Good Life

Translated by Michael Grant

This collection of Cicero's writings discusses duty, friendship, the training of a statesman, and the importance of moral integrity in the search for happiness.

384 pp.   0-14-044244-8 $ 8.95

The Analects

Translated by D. C. Lau

The only reliable account of the philosophy of the legendary Chinese sage, the *Lun-yü (Analects)* constitute a collection of Confucius's sayings compiled by his pupils shortly after his death.

256 pp.   0-14-044348-7 $ 8.95

RENÉ DESCARTES
1596–1650, FRENCH

Discourse on Method and The Meditations

In these essays published in 1637, the father of modern philosophy attacked the prevalent worldview and introduced scientific method to all fields of human inquiry through application of the Cartesian method.

192 pp.   0-14-044206-5 $ 5.95

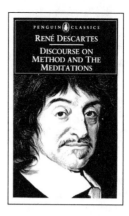

RALPH WALDO EMERSON
1803–1882, AMERICAN

Selected Essays
Edited and introduced by Larzer Ziff

This sampling includes fifteen essays that highlight the formative and significant ideas of this central American thinker: "Nature," "The American Scholar," "An Address Delivered Before the Senior Class in Divinity College, Cambridge," "Man the Reformer," "History," "Self-Reliance," "The Over-Soul," "Circles," "The Transcendentalist," "The Poet," "Experience," "Montaigne; Or, the Skeptic," "Napoleon; Or, the Man of the World," "Fate," and "Thoreau."

360 pp.   0-14-039013-8 $ 9.95

WILLIAM GODWIN
1756–1836, ENGLISH

An Enquiry Concerning Political Justice
And Its Influence on Modern Morals and Happiness

For a description, see HISTORY AND POLITICS.

GEORG WILHELM FRIEDRICH HEGEL
1770–1831, GERMAN

Introductory Lectures on Aesthetics

For a description, see ART AND ARCHITECTURE.

DAVID HUME
1711-1776, SCOTTISH

Dialogues Concerning Natural Religion

Edited and introduced by Martin Bell

Modeled on Cicero's *De Natura Deorum*, this classic treatise on natural religion portrays the eighteenth-century conflict between scientific theism and philosophical skepticism. Hume savages the traditional arguments for the existence of God and suggests that the only religion that can stand up to serious scrutiny is one that is rationally and philosophically derived by the human mind.

160 pp.   0-14-044536-6 $ 7.95

A Treatise of Human Nature

Edited and introduced by Ernest C. Mossner

The first work of this influential philosopher is an unprecedented extension of the Copernican revolution in science to the realm of philosophy.

688 pp.   0-14-043244-2 $ 9.95

RALPH WALDO EMERSON
1803-1882, American

In 1832 Ralph Waldo Emerson, the descendant of a long line of clergy, declared his dissatisfaction with institutionalized religion and resigned as minister of his Boston church. After a year abroad, he settled in the small town of Concord, Massachusetts, and began to develop the ideas which gave birth to the Transcendentalist movement. Celebrating individualism, a personal form of faith, and the essential unity of God, man, and nature, and imbued with a sense of limitless optimism, Transcendentalism was a distinctly American movement, a declaration of independence from European philosophical and literary traditions. In his famous essay "Nature" (1836), Emerson announced, "There are new lands, new men, new thoughts. Let us demand our own works and laws and worship." Emerson's call attracted many of New England's most brilliant and radical thinkers, including Bronson Alcott, George Ripley, Theodore Parker, Margaret Fuller, and Henry Thoreau. His belief in the power of individuals to cultivate the best in themselves and thus change society inspired reform movements that encompassed every aspect of American life, from education to social and political organization, religion to women's rights.

SØREN KIERKEGAARD
1813–1855, DANISH

Either/Or
A Fragment of Life

*Abridged, translated, and introduced by
Alastair Hannay*

The first major work by the precursor of
existentialism examines the philosophical choice between aesthetic and romantic life vs. ethical and domestic life,
and offers profound observations on
the meaning of choice itself.

640 pp.   0-14-044577-3 $ 14.95

Fear and Trembling

*Translated and introduced by
Alastair Hannay*

Abraham's unreserved submission to
God's will provides the focus for this religious and ethical polemic. Originally
written under the pseudonym of Jo-
hannes de Silentio, *Fear and Trembling*
is a key work in the psychology of religious belief.

160 pp.   0-14-044449-1 $ 8.95

Sickness unto Death

*Translated and introduced by
Alastair Hannay*

Arguing that true Christianity exists
only in accordance with free will,
Kierkegaard's stern treatise attacks
Hegelianism and the established
Church, and breaks ground for existen-
tialism and modern theology.

320 pp.   0-14-044533-1 $ 9.95

FRANÇOIS DE LA ROCHEFOUCAULD
1747–1827, FRENCH

Maxims

*Translated and introduced by
L. W. Tancock*

The philosophy of La Rochefoucauld,
which influenced contemporaries as diverse as Voltaire and the Jansenists, is
captured here in more than 600 penetrating and pithy aphorisms.

128 pp.   0-14-044095-X $ 7.95

GEORG CHRISTOPH LICHTENBERG
1742–1799, GERMAN

Aphorisms

*Translated and introduced by
R. J. Hollingdale*

This collection of pithy and witty sayings, by the man who first introduced
the aphorism to Germany, mocks some
of the principal men and movements of
the Enlightenment.

208 pp.   0-14-044519-6 $ 7.95

LUCRETIUS
C. 100 B.C.–C. 55 B.C., ROMAN

On the Nature of the Universe
Translated by R. E.Latham

This edition of the classic poem and seminal text of Epicurean science and philosophy—which shaped human understanding of the world for centuries—brings new textual research and additional context to Lucretius's explorations of spirit, mind, and soul.

320 pp.   0-14-044610-9 $ 11.95

JOHN STUART MILL and JEREMY BENTHAM
1806–1873; 1748–1832, ENGLISH

Utilitarianism and Other Essays
Edited and introduced by Alan Ryan

Bentham's and Mill's influential sociopolitical ideas are set forth in essays and selections from larger works, enhanced by Alan Ryan's extensive introduction analyzing the origins, development, and historical context of these ideas.

352 pp.   0-14-043272-8 $ 9.95

MICHEL DE MONTAIGNE
1533–1592, FRENCH

An Apology for Raymond Sebond
For a description, see HISTORY AND POLITICS.

The Complete Essays
For a description, see LITERATURE.

The Essays: A Selection
For a description, see LITERATURE.

FRIEDRICH NIETZSCHE
1844–1900, GERMAN

Beyond Good and Evil
Newly introduced by Michael Tanner
Translated by R. J. Hollingdale

First published in 1866, this classic work of philosophy still possesses the power to unsettle our notions about existence. Nietzsche discusses how cultures lose their creative drives and become decadent, offering a wealth of fresh insights into such themes as the self-destructive urge of Christianity, the prevalence of "slave moralities," and the dangers of the pursuit of philosophical or scientific truth.

240 pp.   0-14-044513-7 $ 8.95

The Birth of Tragedy
Edited by Michael Tanner
Translated by Shaun Whiteside

Nietzche's first book, published in 1872 and now a seminal work of Western culture, is filled with passionate energy and argument probing the relationship between our experiences of suffering in life and in art, myths, and legends.

160 pp.   0-14-043339-2 $ 8.95

Ecce Homo
For a description, see AUTOBIOGRAPHY AND BIOGRAPHY.

A Nietzsche Reader

Translated, selected, and introduced by R. J. Hollingdale

Designed to give an overview of Nietzsche's thought, of his approach to the conventional problems of Western philosophy, and of his own philosophy of "the will to power," this anthology includes 240 thematically arranged passages from his major philosophical works.

288 pp.   0-14-044329-0 $ 8.95

Thus Spoke Zarathustra

Translated by Walter Kauffmann

Nietzsche's most accessible work, this spiritual odyssey through the modern world influenced such writers as Shaw, D. H. Lawrence, Mann, and Sartre.

352 pp.   0-14-044118-2 $ 9.95

The Twilight of the Idols and The Anti-Christ

Translated and introduced by R. J. Hollingdale

Written in 1888, before he succumbed to insanity, *The Twilight of the Idols* is a fascinating summation of Nietzsche's rejection of the prevalent ideas of his time; *The Anti-Christ* is his passionate challenge to institutional Christianity.

208 pp.   0-14-044514-5 $ 9.95

BLAISE PASCAL
1632–1662, FRENCH

Pensées

For a description see RELIGION.

PLATO
C. 428 B.C.–C. 348 B.C., GREEK

Early Socratic Dialogues

Edited and introduced by Trevor J. Saunders

Rich in drama and humor, seven dialogues provide a definitive portrait of Socrates' thought and times. The selection includes: *Ion, Laches, Lysis, Charmides, Hippias Major, Hippias Minor,* and *Euthydemus.*

400 pp.   0-14-044447-5 $ 9.95

Gorgias

Translated and introduced by Walter Hamilton

Though Gorgias was a teacher of oratory, the dialogue is more concerned with ethics than with the art of public speaking.

160 pp.   0-14-044094-1 $ 7.95

The Last Days of Socrates
Euthyphro/The Apology/Crito/Phaedo

*Translated by Hugh Tredennick and
Harold Tarrant
Introduced by Harold Tarrant*

Containing the four superb Platonic dialogues that form the classic account of
the trial and death of Socrates, this volume presents a revised translation, with
extensive notes, of the best known
works of Western thought.

256 pp.   0-14-044582-X $ 9.95

The Laws

*Translated and introduced by
Trevor J. Saunders*

In his last and longest work, Plato set
forth a detailed code of immutable laws
for the ideal state that contrasts sharply
with the notion of the philosopher-king
developed in *The Republic*. This edition
includes a list of crimes and punish-
ments and an appendix of Plato's letters.

558 pp.   0-14-044222-7 $ 8.95

Phaedrus and Letters VII and VIII

*Translated and introduced by
Walter Hamilton*

Phaedrus, chiefly valued for its idyllic
setting and magnificent myth, is concerned with establishing the principles
of rhetoric based on the knowledge of
truth inspired by love. The seventh and
eighth letters reflect Plato's involvement
in Sicilian politics and reveal fascinating
glimpses into the contemporary power
struggle.

160 pp.   0-14-044275-8 $ 9.95

Philebus

*Translated and introduced by
Robin H. Waterfield*

This is Plato's most deliberate and thor-
ough attempt to describe the good life
and the way people ought to achieve it,
along with an extensive critical Introduction covering the main stages of the
dialogue.

160 pp.   0-14-044395-9 $ 5.95

Protagoras and Meno

*Translated and introduced by
W. K. C. Guthrie*

These two dialogues explore the ques-
tion of virtue, the first leading to the
conclusion that all virtues are united by
knowledge, the second propounding
the point of view that virtue is teach-
able.

160 pp.   0-14-044068-2 $ 8.95

The Republic

*Translated and introduced by
Desmond Lee*

The first great piece of utopian writing,
Plato's treatise on an ideal state applies
philosophical principles to political affairs.

472 pp.   0-14-044048-8 $ 6.95

The Symposium

*Translated and introduced by
Walter Hamilton*

A complete and complex philosophy of
love emerges from a series of speeches
by the guests—including Socrates and
Alcibiades—at an Athenian dinner
party.

128 pp.   0-14-044024-0 $ 6.95

Theaetetus

Translated with a critical essay by
Robin Waterfield

Plato examines the idea of knowledge, putting forth and criticizing opposing definitions in this pioneering work in epistemology.

256 pp.   0-14-044450-5 $ 6.95

Timaeus and Critias

Translated and introduced by
Desmond Lee

The earliest Greek account of a divine creation, *Timaeus* is concerned with cosmology and anthropology. The unfinished *Critias*, Plato's only work on the natural sciences, tells the story of the lost civilization of Atlantis.

176 pp.   0-14-044261-8 $ 8.95

PLOTINUS
205–270, ROMAN

The Enneads

Edited by John Dillon
Translated by Stephen MacKenna

Here is a highly original synthesis of Platonism, mystic passion, ideas from Greek philosophy, and variants of the Trinity and other central tenets of Christian doctrine by the brilliant thinker who has had an immense influence on mystics and religious writers.

688 pp.   0-14-044520-X $ 13.95

JEAN-JACQUES
ROUSSEAU
1712–1788, FRENCH

The Confessions

For a description, see AUTOBIOGRAPHY AND BIOGRAPHY.

A Discourse on Inequality

Translated, annotated, and introduced by
Maurice Cranston

The most influential of Rousseau's writings, the "Second Discourse" set forth a theory of human evolution that prefigured the discoveries of Darwin, revolutionized the study of anthropology and linguistics, and made a seminal contribution to political and social thought—leading to both the French Revolution and the birth of social science.

208 pp.   0-14-044439-4 $ 8.95

Reveries of the Solitary Walker

Translated and introduced by
Peter France

Ten meditations written in the two years before Rousseau's death in 1778 provide an excellent introduction to the thinker's complex world, expressing in its full force the agony of isolation and alienation.

160 pp.   0-14-044363-0 $ 7.95

The Social Contract

Translated and introduced by Maurice Cranston

The crowning work of Rousseau's political philosophy, *The Social Contract* describes the basic principles of democratic government, stressing that law derives from the will of the people.

192 pp.   0-14-044201-4 $ 6.95

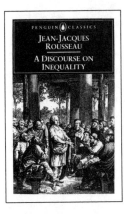

PENGUIN CLASSICS
JEAN-JACQUES ROUSSEAU
A DISCOURSE ON INEQUALITY

ARTHUR SCHOPENHAUER
1788–1860, GERMAN

Essays and Aphorisms

Selected and translated by R. J. Hollingdale

This selection of thoughts on religion, ethics, politics, women, suicide, books, and much more is taken from Schopenhauer's last work, *Parerga and Paralipomena,* published in 1851.

240 pp.   0-14-044227-8 $ 9.95

SENECA
C. 4 B.C.– A.D.65, ROMAN

Letters from a Stoic

Translated by Robin Campbell

Ranging from lively epistles to serious essays, these 124 letters selected from *Epistulae Morales ad Lucilium* espouse the philosophy of Stoicism. This volume includes Tacitus's account of Seneca's death.

256 pp.   0-14-044210-3 $ 8.95

HENRY DAVID THOREAU
1817–1862, AMERICAN

Walden and Civil Disobedience

Introduced by Michael Meyer

Two classic examinations of individuality in relation to nature, society, and government are expounded by a seminal American thinker.

440 pp.   0-14-039044-8 $ 8.95

A Year in Thoreau's Journal

For a description, see LITERATURE.

VOLTAIRE
1694–1778, FRENCH

Philosophical Dictionary

Translated, edited, and introduced by Theodore Besterman

Voltaire's irony, scrutiny, and passionate love of reason and justice are fully evident in this deliberately revolutionary series of essays on religion, metaphysics, society, and government.

400 pp.   0-14-044257-X $ 10.95

MARY WOLLSTONECRAFT
1759–1797, ENGLISH

A Vindication of the Rights of Woman

Edited by Miriam Kramnick

Published in 1792, this classic treatise applied the egalitarian principles of the French and American revolutions to the social, political, and economic conditions of women.

320 pp.   0-14-043199-3 $ 5.95

MARY WOLLSTONECRAFT and WILLIAM GODWIN
1759–1797, ENGLISH
1756–1836, ENGLISH

A Short Residence in Sweden, Norway, and Denmark and Memoirs of the Author of *A Vindication of the Rights of Woman*

Edited and introduced by Richard Holmes

Feminist writer Wollstonecraft's record of her Scandinavian journey and her philosopher-husband's memoirs (written after her death) offer insight into the minds of two major figures in the transition from reason to romanticism in Europe.

320 pp.   0-14-043269-8 $ 7.95

MARY WOLLSTONECRAFT
1759–1797, English

"Two books made Mary Wollstonecraft famous: *A Vindication of the Rights of Woman*, the first real feminist manifesto, which she published in London in 1792 before travelling to Paris to experience the French Revolution; and the *Memoirs* written by her husband, William Godwin, after her death in childbirth in 1797, which revealed to a scandalized world just how unconventional her life had been. As a thinker on social issues, Wollstonecraft was bold and original, and expressed her views through essays, fiction, and travel writing. She is also remembered for her letters, which show her as a tender lover and mother, passionate and vulnerable. The combination of strict thinking and Romantic sensibility is powerful, and the link with the Romantic movement was actually embodied in her daughter, Mary, author of the classic novel *Frankenstein* and wife of the poet Shelley."—**Claire Tomalin**

Conversations of Socrates

*Translated by Hugh Tredennick and
Robin Waterfield
Edited and introduced by
Robin Waterfield*

Xenophon's complete Socratic works—
*Socrates' Defence, Memoirs of Socrates,
The Dinner Party,* and *The Estate-Manager*—not only portray the character
and teachings of the great philosopher
but apply Socratic principles to the
daily life of Greece, giving insight into
the religious, political, and moral views
of the Athenians.

384 pp.   0-14-044517-X $ 10.95

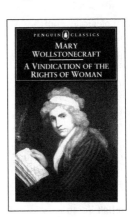

A Celtic Miscellany

*Translated and annotated by Kenneth
Hurlstone Jackson*

More than 240 thematically arranged
selections of Celtic poetry and prose,
translated from the Welsh, Irish, and
Scottish Gaelic and the Cornish, Breton,
and Manx languages, provide insight
into the Celtic mind from the earliest
times to the nineteenth century.

352 pp.   0-14-044247-2 $ 10.95

The Earliest English Poems
Third Revised Edition

*Translated and introduced by
Michael Alexander*

This select volume includes translations
of heroic poems (including the oldest
poem in the English language), a passage from Beowulf, "riddles" from *The
Exeter Book*, and elegies in Anglo-Saxon
meter and alliteration.

176 pp.   0-14-044594-3 $ 8.95

Eighteenth-Century English Verse

*Edited and introduced by
Dennis Davison*

In this selection, 163 poets, including
the famous as well as the lesser-known,
explore the major themes of eighteenth-
century poetry.

320 pp.   0-14-042169-6 $ 6.95

English Romantic Verse

Edited and introduced by David Wright

Nearly all the famous and beloved masterworks can be found here—*Intimations of Immortality*, *The Ancient Mariner*, and *The Tyger*—as well as some less familiar poems.

384 pp.   0-14-042102-5 $ 7.95

The Exeter Book of Riddles
A Revised Edition

Translated and introduced by Kevin Crossley-Holland

The eleventh-century manuscript of Old English verses, kept in the cathedral at Exeter, is one of the most famous treasures of the medieval period. Now the works—wide-ranging in style and content—are newly translated, with extensive historical and literary notes.

160 pp.   0-14-043367-8 $ 10.95

French Poetry
1820–1950

Edited by William Rees

Featuring both French text and English prose translations, this remarkable anthology covers a broad range of poetry in the French tradition.

856 pp.   0-14-042357-5 $ 16.95

The Golden Treasury
The Best Songs and Lyrical Poems in the English Language

*Edited and introduced by Christopher Ricks
Selected and arranged with notes by Francis Turner Palgrave*

Unrivalled as the paradigm of poetry anthologies, the *Treasury* includes some of the finest English lyric verse from the Elizabethan era to the mid-nineteenth century.

528 pp.   0-14-042364-8 $ 11.95

The Greek Anthology

Edited by Peter Jay

Arranged chronologically from the seventh century B.C. to the sixth century A.D. 850 epitaphs, satires, jokes, pastoral epigrams, and poems of love and friendship have been translated by distinguished American and British poets for this largest selection of *The Greek Anthology* ever published in verse translation.

446 pp.   0-14-044285-5 $ 10.95

Medieval English Verse

Edited by Brian Stone

Religious and secular lyrics, short narrative poems, and moral, political, and comic verses are all included in this comprehensive collection of works from the thirteenth and fourteenth centuries.

256 pp.   0-14-044144-1 $ 11.95

The Metaphysical Poets

Edited by Helen Gardner

These select works feature thirty-eight poets, among them Carew, Crashaw, Donne, Herbert, Jonson, Lovelace, Marvell, Suckling, and Vaughan.

332 pp.   0-14-042038-X $ 7.95

New Songs from a Jade Terrace

Critical essay by J. H. Prynne
Translated and introduced by
Anne Birrell

Originally compiled in A.D. 545, this anthology tracing the development of Chinese love poetry is in English for the first time.

432 pp.   0-14-044487-4 $ 6.95

The Penguin Book of First World War Poetry

Edited and introduced by Jon Silkin

These selections have been culled from the works of thirty-eight British, European, and American writers—Hardy, Kipling, Rupert Brooke, Siegfried Sassoon, and Wilfred Owen among them.

20TH-CENTURY CLASSICS

270 pp.   0-14-018367-1 $ 11.95

The Penguin Book of Renaissance Verse 1509–1659

Edited by H. R. Woudhuysen
Selected and introduced by
David Norbrook

This superbly edited anthology offers a comprehensive view of one of the most fertile periods in the history of literature. Generous space is devoted to writings of women, works of popular culture, and regional non-courtly poetry.

960 pp.   0-14-042346-X $ 19.95

Poem of the Cid

Translated and introduced by Rita Hamilton and Janet Perry

This epic poem, the only one to have survived from medieval Spain, depicts the career of the warlord El Cid, in a unique blend of fiction and historical fact. Both English and Spanish texts are provided.

256 pp.   0-14-044446-7 $ 8.95

Poems from the Sanskrit

Translated and edited by John Brough

Written between the fourth and tenth centuries A.D., these secular poems illustrate the great diversity of subject matter, style, and imagination of classical Sanskrit literature.

160 pp.   0-14-044198-0 $ 9.95

Poems of the Late T'ang

Translated and edited by A. C. Graham

This volume introduces seven poets who flourished during the eighth and ninth centuries, the latter part of the golden age of Chinese literature.

176 pp.   0-14-044157-3 $ 6.95

Roman Poets of the Early Empire

Edited and introduced by A. J. Boyle and J. P. Sullivan

In this stimulating anthology, underrated poets of the so-called Silver Age—Seneca, Petronius, Lucan, Statius, and others—emerge from obscurity.

480 pp.   0-14-044544-7 $ 10.95

Selections from the Carmina Burana
A New Verse Translation

Translated and edited by David Parlett

Wine, women, love, and nature are recurring themes in fifty-two selections from the thirteenth-century *Carmina Burana*, the largest, most varied surviving anthology of medieval Latin poetry.

272 pp.   0-14-044440-8 $ 8.95

Surrealist Poetry in English

Edited and introduced by Edward B. Germain

This comprehensive anthology of the works of American and English surrealist poets, from the 1930s to the present, includes poetry by Ted Berrigan, Frank O'Hara, Robert Bly, Randall Jarrell, and John Ashbery, among others.

20TH-CENTURY CLASSICS

352 pp.   0-14-018486-4 $ 12.95

Victorian Verse
A Critical Anthology

Edited by George Macbeth

This anthology of the work of sixty-five famous and lesser-known poets emphasizes the sheer inventiveness of the Victorians and shows how many of the best poets explored forbidden subjects—violence, religious doubt, eroticism, crime, passion—through dramatic monologue and in the narrative poem.

448 pp.   0-14-042110-6 $ 10.95

Selected Poems

*Translated and introduced by
D. M. Thomas*

Akhmatova's poems bear witness to the terrors of Stalinism, the loss of all whom she loved, and to the blessings of memory. These outstanding translations by novelist D. M. Thomas do honor to the works of the greatest woman poet in modern history.

20TH-CENTURY CLASSICS

160 pp.   0-14-018617-4 $ 9.95

Selected Poems

Edited by Timothy Peltason

A selection of Arnold's best and most memorable poems, this collection includes such major works as "Dover Beach" and "Thyrsis" and the full texts of the long poems "Empedocles on Etna," "Sohrab and Rustum," and "Tristram and Iseult."

256 pp.   0-14-042376-1 $ 9.95

Selected Poems

*Translated, selected, and
introduced by Joanna Richardson*

The themes, style, and often shocking revelations of *Les Fleurs du Mal, Les Épaves,* and the miscellaneous poems collected in this bilingual edition make it clear why Baudelaire is often considered the first modern poet.

256 pp.   0-14-042188-2 $ 8.95

The Hermit and The Love-Thief

*Translated and introduced by
Barbara Stoler Miller*

The Sanskrit poems of Bhartrihari, a fifth-century philosopher, and Bilhana, an eleventh-century poet, are brought together in one volume as outstanding examples of the classical Indian genre known as the fragmentary lyric.

144 pp.   0-14-044584-6 $ 6.95

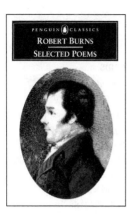

BIHĀRI
C. 1595–1664, INDIAN

The Satasai

*Translated and introduced by
K. P. Bahadur*

In this dual language collection are more than 700 Hindi love poems—exuberant, sensual, courtly, raw, refined— comparable to the *Kama Sutra* and the verse of Ovid, and written by the foremost poet of seventeenth-century India.

416 pp.   0-14-044576-5 $ 11.95

WILLIAM BLAKE
1757–1827, ENGLISH

The Complete Poems

Edited by Alicia Ostriker

This complete anthology contains all of Blake's poetry, with more than 150 pages of explanatory notes, including plot outlines of the more difficult poems, a chronology of Blake's life, a supplementary reading list, and a dictionary of proper names.

1,072 pp.   0-14-042215-3 $ 12.95

EMILY BRONTË
1818–1848, ENGLISH

The Complete Poems

Edited and introduced by Janet Gezari

The first major edition in half a century, here is a collection of twenty-one passionate poems by Brontë—first published under pseudonym in 1846—now newly annotated and introduced.

352 pp.   0-14-042352-4 $ 10.95

ROBERT BROWNING
1812–1889, ENGLISH

The Poems

*Edited by John Pettigrew
Revised by Thomas J. Collins and
John Pettigrew*

The first completely annotated edition of Browning's work, these two volumes present the full scope of the poet's stylistic achievements and his vitality, boldness, and acute psychological understanding.

Vol. 1:   1,232 pp. 0-14-042259-5 $ 16.95
Vol. 2:   1,208 pp. 0-14-042260-9 $ 14.95

The Ring and the Book

*Edited and introduced by
Richard D. Altick*

This first fully annotated version of Browning's masterpiece provides a great deal of detailed help with the poet's lively but often eccentric language and tackles the challenges of Browning's wide range of curious information and his immense and flexible vocabulary.

712 pp.   0-14-042294-3 $ 10.95

ROBERT BURNS
1759–1796, SCOTTISH

Selected Poems
Edited by Carol McGuirk

Arranged in probable order of composition, and featuring both lyrics and tunes, this collection of poems and songs written by Burns late in his career reveals his true voice for modern readers. With chronology and glossary.

368 pp.   0-14-042382-6 $ 9.95

GEORGE GORDEN, LORD BYRON
1788–1824, ENGLISH

Don Juan
Edited by T. G. Steffan, E. Steffan, and W. W. Pratt
Introduced by T. G. Steffan

A significant contribution to scholarship, this extensively annotated edition covers variant readings and Byron's massive historical allusions.

760 pp.   0-14-042216-1 $ 11.95

CATULLUS
C. 84 B.C.–54 B.C., ROMAN

The Poems of Catullus
Translated by Peter Whigham

These 111 poems introduce the lyric poet Catullus, master of the pungent epigram, who found his inspiration in the glittering Roman society of the late Republic.

254 pp.   0-14-044180-8 $ 9.95

AUSTIN CLARKE
1896–1974, IRISH

Selected Poems
Edited and introduced by Hugh Maxton

This is a fully annotated collection of works by the writer generally considered the finest Irish poet of the generation following Yeats.

20TH-CENTURY CLASSICS
288 pp.   0-14-018649-2 $ 11.95

ARTHUR HUGH CLOUGH
1819–1861, ENGLISH

Selected Poems
Edited by Jim McCue

Rich in irony and skepticism, the poetry of Arthur Hugh Clough constitutes an investigation into Victorian values, codes of behavior, and the nature of faith. This volume contains a generous selection of his short lyrics and satires.

272 pp.   0-14-042374-5 $ 10.95

GEORGE CRABBE
1754–1832, ENGLISH

Selected Poems
Edited and introduced by Gavin Edwards

Dramatizing human motive in the subtlest of language, this selection of poems includes *Sir Eustace Grey*, the complete *Tales in Verse of 1812*, and the remarkable late work *The Family of Love*.

544 pp.   0-14-042365-6 $ 12.95

DANTE
1265–1321, FLORENTINE

La Vita Nuova

Translated by Barbara Reynolds

This series of astonishing and tender love poems to Beatrice is interspersed with Dante's own explanations of their sources and detailed analyses of their structure.

128 pp.   0-14-044216-2 $ 7.95

JOHN DONNE
1572–1631, ENGLISH

The Complete English Poems

Edited by A. J. Smith

Written in the natural rhythms of the speaking voice, Donne's poetry is of particular appeal to the modern reader; many consider him the greatest writer of love poetry of all time.

680 pp.   0-14-042209-9 $ 11.95

ABDUL FERDOWSI
c. 940–1020, PERSIAN

The Legend of Seyavash

Translated and introduced by Dick Davis

The epic story of a Persian prince, a warrior with conscience and extraordinary psychological insight, is Persia's own *Iliad*. This legend lies at the heart of the national saga, *The Shahnameh*.

176 pp.   0-14-044566-8 $ 8.95

JOHANN W. VON GOETHE
1749–1832, GERMAN

Selected Verse

Translated by David Luke

This dual language edition of nearly three hundred poems draws from every period of Goethe's work, including substantial portions of *Faust*.

368 pp.   0-14-042074-6 $ 10.95

HEINRICH HEINE
1797–1856, GERMAN

Selected Verse

Translated and introduced by Peter Branscombe

Including poems in their original German, along with English prose translations, this anthology provides the perfect introduction to this towering figure of the revolutionary literary movement Young Germany.

294 pp.   0-14-042098-3 $ 9.95

ROBERT HENRYSON
c. 1425-1508, SCOTTISH

The Testament of Cresseid and Other Poems
Selected by Hugh MacDiarmid

This collection of fifteenth-century poems features Henryson's pendant to *Troilus and Criseyde*, 600 lines of rhyme royal notable for its controversial moralization and tragic interpretation of the Chaucer poem.

96 pp.   0-14-044507-2 $ 5.95

GEORGE HERBERT
1593-1633, ENGLISH

The Complete English Poems
Edited and introduced by John Tobin

The Temple, Herbert's masterpiece of worldly anguish and divine transcendence; his uncollected English verse; *A Priest to the Temple* (prose); and selections from Herbert's Latin poetry with translations, form the basis of this volume.

496 pp.   0-14-042348-6 $ 11.95

HESIOD and THEOGNIS
c. 8TH CENT. B.C.; 6TH CENT. B.C., GREEK

Hesiod and Theognis
Translated by Dorothea Wender

Together these two poets offer a superb introduction to the life and thought of Greece.

176 pp.   0-14-044283-9 $ 8.95

GERARD MANLEY HOPKINS
1844-1889, ENGLISH

Poems and Prose
Edited by W. H. Gardner

This edition contains verse wrought from the creative tensions and paradoxes of a poet-priest whose "creative violence" has been compared to that of Dylan Thomas.

266 pp.   0-14-042015-0 $ 12.95

HORACE
65 B.C.-8 B.C., ROMAN

The Complete Odes and Epodes
Introduced by Betty Radice
Translated by W. G. Shepherd

The elusive personality and ironic philosophy of Horace are exemplified in 17 epodes, 103 odes, and *The Centennial Hymn*.

256 pp.   0-14-044422-X $ 9.95

HORACE and PERSIUS
65 B.C.-8 B.C., ROMAN
c. 212 B.C.-c. 165 B.C., MACEDONIAN

The Satires of Horace and Persius
Translated by Niall Rudd

The broad range of the controversial Roman poetic form the satura is illustrated in 18 satires and 23 epistles of Horace, and 6 metaphorical essays of the Stoic critic Persius, presented in modern verse translation.

304 pp.   0-14-044279-0 $ 9.95

JAMES WELDON JOHNSON
1871–1938, AMERICAN

God's Trombones
Seven Negro Sermons in Verse
Illustrated by Aaron Douglas

First collected as poetry in the 1940s, these works preserve the great oral tradition of African-American preachers and represent a significant part of African-American folk art; they are often dramatized and recorded.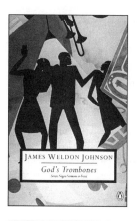

20TH-CENTURY CLASSICS

64 pp.   0-14-018403-1 $ 6.95

Saint Peter Relates an Incident
Selected Poems

These passionate poems, first published in one volume in 1935 during the heyday of the Harlem Renaissance, include both uncompromising indictments of racist injustice and celebratory songs of black life and African-American achievement by poet, novelist, editor, and critic Johnson.

20TH-CENTURY CLASSICS

112 pp.   0-14-018684-0 $ 8.95

SAMUEL JOHNSON
1709–1784, ENGLISH

The Complete English Poems
Edited and introduced by J. D. Fleeman

These works in verse by eighteenth-century England's charismatic critic and lexicographer Samuel Johnson include his savage satire, *London,* and the tragic poem *The Vanity of Human Wishes.*

272 pp.   0-14-042296-X $ 11.95

BEN JONSON
1572–1637, ENGLISH

The Complete Poems
Edited with a preface and notes by George Parfitt

Nearly 400 works display the characteristic blend of classical and contemporary ideals that imbues Jonson's work, including *Epigrams, The Forest, Underwoods: Miscellaneous Poems, Horace, The Art of Poetry,* and *Timber: Or Discoveries.*

640 pp.   0-14-042277-3 $ 12.95

The Sixteen Satires

Translated and introduced by
Peter Green

Written during the reigns of Trajan and Hadrian, these satires present a vivid portrait of the splendor, squalor, and complexity of life in the closing years of the century.

320 pp.   0-14-044194-8 $ 9.95

The Complete Poems
Second Edition

Edited by John Barnard

In addition to all the poems and plays known to be written by the archetypal Romantic poet, this edition includes long extracts from Keats's letters, his annotations to *Paradise Lost*, and two poems and a play fragment that have been attributed to him.

754 pp.   0-14-042210-2 $ 10.95

JOHN KEATS

1795–1821, English

"Two facts about John Keats: his life coincided almost exactly with a period of British history more turbulent than any since the Civil War. He spent as long training to become a doctor as he did practicing as a poet. These things complicate the late-Victorian view of him as the most luxurious of the Romantic writers—someone whose work dropped from a clear sky untouched by contemporary circumstances. Yet his reputation as a pure sensualist is still remarkably intact, and is often justified by reference to his famous appeal for "a life of sensations rather than thoughts." In fact Keats's longing for "sensation" expresses his appetite for a particular kind of thought, not for no thought at all. He wanted to think in a way that proved ideas on his pulses, so that he could feel things to be true, not merely understand them to be true. When we relish the sensuality of his poems, therefore, we should be alert to this very unpalpable design they have on us. As they show us the ways in which life mixes pain with pleasure, they tell us about a critical moment in our history, and about the ambitions of a poet who wished to be a physician by other than medical means.—**Andrew Motion**

COMTE DE LAUTRÉAMONT
1847–1870, FRENCH

Maldoror and Poems

Translated and introduced by Paul Knight

One of the earliest and most astonishing examples of surrealist writing, Lautréamont's hallucinatory tale *Maldoror* was hailed as a work of genius by Gide, Breton, Modigliani, and Verlaine. This edition includes a translation of the epigrammatic *Poésies*.

288 pp.   0-14-044342-8 $ 8.95

D. H. LAWRENCE
1885–1930, ENGLISH

Complete Poems

Collected, edited, and introduced with notes by Vivian de Sola Pinto and F. Warren Roberts

This definitive collection of Lawrence's poems, with appendixes containing juvenilia, variants and early drafts, and Lawrence's own critical introductions to his poems, also includes full textual and explanatory notes, glossary, and index for the work of one of the greatest poets of the twentieth century.

20TH-CENTURY CLASSICS

1,088 pp.   0-14-018657-3 $ 19.95

LI PO and TU FU
701–762; 712–770, CHINESE

Li Po and Tu Fu
Poems

Translated and introduced by Arthur Cooper

More than forty selections from two eighth-century poets of China cover the whole spectrum of human life and feeling.

256 pp.   0-14-044272-3 $ 8.95

HENRY W. LONGFELLOW
1807–1882, AMERICAN

Selected Poems

Edited and introduced by Laurence Buell

Longfellow was the most popular poet of his day. This selection includes generous samplings from his longer works—*Evangeline*, *The Courtship of Miles Standish*, and *Hiawatha*—as well as his shorter lyrics and less familiar narrative poems.

240 pp.   0-14-039064-2 $ 9.95

OSIP MANDELSTAM
1891–1938, RUSSIAN

Selected Poems
Translated by James Greene

A selection of poetry by the great lyric poet of revolutionary Russia, Mandelstam's work had been suppressed for more than forty years.

20TH-CENTURY CLASSICS

144 pp.   0-14-018474-0 $ 9.95

CHRISTOPHER MARLOWE
1564–1593, ENGLISH

The Complete Poems and Translations
Edited by Stephen Orgel

All Marlowe's poems and translations are presented in a conservatively modernized text along with two contemporary continuations of *Hero and Leander* and several replies to *The Passionate Shepherd*.

288 pp.   0-14-042267-6 $ 9.95

MARTIAL
1ST CENT., ROMAN

The Epigrams
Translated by James Michie

Scabrous, affectionate, cruel, playful, Martial's highly polished epigrams celebrate the modern megalopolis that was first-century Rome. Latin originals appear alongside English translations in this dual language edition.

208 pp.   0-14-044350-9 $ 8.95

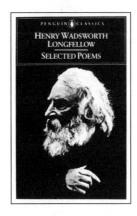

ANDREW MARVELL
1621–1678, ENGLISH

The Complete Poems
Edited by Elizabeth Story Donno

Based on recent studies of existing manuscripts, this collection of works by the seventeenth-century poet much admired by T. S. Eliot includes modern translations of Marvell's Greek and Latin poems, as well as his works in English.

320 pp.   0-14-042213-7 $ 9.95

MATSUO BASHŌ
1644–1694, JAPANESE

On Love and Barley
Haiku of Bashō

Translated and introduced by Lucien Stryk

These 253 selections reveal Bashō's mastery of the genre.

96 pp.   0-14-044459-9 $ 7.95

The Narrow Road to the Deep North and Other Travel Sketches

Translated by Nobuyuki Yuasa

Bashō's haiku are a series of superb pictures in which whole landscapes and seasons are evoked by description of the crucial details.

176 pp.   0-14-044185-9 $ 9.95

MARIANNE MOORE
1887–1972, AMERICAN

Complete Poems

This definitive edition contains sixty years of Marianne Moore's poems, incorporating her text revisions and her own entertaining notes that reveal the inspiration for complete poems and individual lines.

20TH-CENTURY CLASSICS

320 pp.   0-14-018851-7 $ 12.95

PABLO NERUDA
1904–1973, CHILEAN

Twenty Love Poems and a Song of Despair

Translated by W. S. Merwin

This edition of Neruda's most enduring and popular work—love poems of daring symbolism and sensuality—contains the original Spanish text, and on facing pages the English translation.

20TH-CENTURY CLASSICS

88 pp.   0-14-018648-4 $ 8.95

OMAR KHAYYÁM
C. 1048–C. 1131, ARAB

The Rubáiyát of Omar Khayyám

Translated and introduced by Peter Avery and John Heath-Stubbs

This contemporary edition of Khayyám has been selected and translated by Persian scholar Avery and poet Heath-Stubbs.

120 pp.   0-14-044384-3 $ 7.95

OVID
43 B.C.– A.D. 17, ROMAN

The Erotic Poems

Translated and introduced by Peter Green

These works by Ovid—*Ars Amatoria, the Amores, Cures for Love,* and *On Facial Treatment for Ladies*—give testament to the foremost erotic poet of the Augustan period.

464 pp.   0-14-044360-6 $ 9.95

Heroides

Translated and introduced with notes by Harold Isbell

Dramatic monologues in the form of love letters written between mythological lovers, such as Paris and Helen and Hero and Leander, reveal Ovid's gift for psychological insight.

288 pp.   0-14-042355-9 $ 8.95

The Poems of Exile

For a description, see LITERATURE.

BORIS PASTERNAK
1890–1960, RUSSIAN

Pasternak
Selected Poems

Translated by Jon Stallworthy and Peter France

These varied selections share a continuity of themes and values that encapsulate Nobel Prize laureate Boris Pasternak's vivid, sensual response to the world surrounding him.

20TH-CENTURY CLASSICS

160 pp.   0-14-018466-X $ 8.95

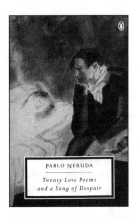

PABLO NERUDA

*Twenty Love Poems
and a Song of Despair*

PINDAR
C. 533 B.C.–C. 438 B.C., GREEK

QU YUAN and OTHER POETS
C. 1ST–2ND CENTURY, A.D., CHINESE

The Odes

Translated and introduced by C. M. Bowra

The entire spectrum of Greek moral order, from earthly competition to fate and mythology, is covered in Pindar's *Epinicia*—choral songs extolling victories in the games at Olympia, Delphi, Nemea, and Corinth.

256 pp.   0-14-044209-X $ 9.95

The Songs of the South
An Anthology of Ancient Chinese Poems by Qu Yuan and Other Poets

Translated and introduced by David Hawks

First compiled in the second century A.D., *The Songs of the South* contains ancient poems from one of the two great traditions in Chinese poetry and features many poems attributed to Qu Yuan, honored as China's first poet.

352 pp.   0-14-044375-4 $ 11.95

PROPERTIUS
C. 50 B.C.–C. 15 B.C., ROMAN

The Poems

Translated with notes by W. G. Shepherd

Poems written with a sensitivity to sound and imagery that transcended the limits of traditional Latin poetry create an unforgettable picture of a brilliant but tormented man.

224 pp.   0-14-044464-5 $ 9.95

ARTHUR RIMBAUD
1854–1891, FRENCH

Collected Poems

Translated and introduced by
Oliver Bernard

All the Symbolist poet's known poems
are included in this volume—except for
a few schoolboy Latin pieces—along
with a selection of Rimbaud's letters.
Both letters and poems are presented in
English prose translations as well as the
original French.

384 pp.   0-14-042064-9 $ 10.95

SIR PHILIP SIDNEY
1554–1586, ENGLISH

Selected Poems

Edited and introduced by
Catherine Bates

This volume of the poems of Sir Philip
Sidney, soldier, statesman, and Renaissance ideal—the man of action and the
man of letters—includes readable,
modernized versions of his most famous works, and the complete *Astrophel
and Stella,* the first sonnet sequence in
the English language.

224 pp.   0-14-042378-8 $ 9.95

JOHN SKELTON
1460–1529, ENGLISH

The Complete English Poems

Edited and introduced by
John Scattergood

These elegant, often playful poems,
early masterpieces of English literature,
form a bridge between medieval and
Elizabethan verse. The morality play
Magnyfycence is included.

576 pp.   0-14-042233-1 $ 12.95

CHRISTOPHER SMART
1722–1771, ENGLISH

Selected Poems

Edited by Katrina Williamson and
Marcus Walsh

One of the most startlingly original poets of the eighteenth century, Smart
produced some of his finest hymns,
psalms, and religious poems (including
Song to David) while confined to asy-
lums or debtors' prison.

400 pp.   0-14-042367-2 $ 10.95

EDMUND SPENSER
c. 1552–1599, ENGLISH

The Faerie Queene
*Edited by Thomas P. Roche, Jr.,
with C. Patrick O'Connell, Jr.*

The first English-language epic,
Spenser's masterful extended allegory of
knightly virtue and supreme grace brilliantly bridges the span from medieval
romance to Renaissance opus.

1,248 pp.   0-14-042207-2 $ 14.95

JONATHAN SWIFT
1667–1745, ENGLISH

Complete Poems
Edited and introduced by Pat Rogers

This complete edition encompasses the
poetic works of one of the greatest English-language moralists and satirists.

960 pp.   0-14-042261-7 $ 16.95

Selected Poems
Edited and introduced by Pat Rogers

This fully annotated collection of poetry
by the author of *Gulliver's Travels* and
other works of satirical genius includes
savage political broadsides, scandalous
scatalogical pieces, and the longer literary achievements of his later years.

240 pp.   0-14-042377-X $ 10.95

RABINDRANATH TAGORE
1861–1941, INDIAN

Selected Poems
*Edited, introduced, and translated by
William Radice*

Forty-eight selections cover the period
1882–1941 and provide a long-overdue
reappraisal of the Bengali Noble Prize
winner's poetry.

20TH-CENTURY CLASSICS
224 pp.   0-14-018366-3 $ 9.95

ALFRED, LORD TENNYSON
1809–1892, ENGLISH

Idylls of the King
Edited by J. M. Gray

Arthur's story is retold through Tennyson's poetic embodiment of the universal and unending war between sense
and soul.

376 pp.   0-14-042253-6 $ 7.95

ALFRED, LORD TENNYSON
1809–1892, English

T. S. Eliot, retrieving Tennyson from years of prejudice and neglect, described
him as "the most instinctive rebel against the society in which he was the
most perfect conformist." Before he threw away his genius by attempting to
conform to the Victorian ideal of a Poet Laureate, Tennyson wrote some of
the most beautiful lyrics in the language. His best poetry is personal, nonmoral, exotic, and sublimely resistant to literary criticism or psychoanalysis.

Selected Poems

Edited by Aidan Day

From a genius at painting human emotions in rich and sensuous imagery, this volume focuses on *In Memoriam* (1850), a record of spiritual conflict considered to be Tennyson's greatest work.

400 pp.   0-14-044545-5 $ 10.95

THEOCRITUS
C. 310 B.C.–250 B.C., GREEK

The Idylls

Translated and introduced by Robert Wells

From Sicilian legend to the sexual gossip of herdsmen, these second-century B.C. pastorals are presented in modern verse translations that reveal Theocritus as a varied and compelling poet.

160 pp.   0-14-044523-4 $ 8.95

MARINA TSVETAEVA
1892–1941, RUSSIAN

Selected Poems

Translated and introduced by Elaine Feinstein

An admired contemporary of Rilke, Akhmatova, and Mandelstam, Russian poet Marina Tsvetaeva bore witness to the turmoil and devastation of the Revolution, and chronicled her difficult life in exile, sustained by the inspiration and power of her modern verse.

20TH-CENTURY CLASSICS

160 pp.   0-14-018759-6 $ 11.95

HENRY VAUGHAN
1621–1695, ENGLISH

The Complete Poems

Edited by Alan Rudrum

This comprehensive anthology includes Vaughan's best-known work, *Silex Scintillans*, and other religious poems, as well as a selection of secular verses and translations. Alan Rudrum has meticulously annotated the biblical sources of Vaughan's allusions and images, enhancing the reader's understanding and appreciation of the poetry.

720 pp.   0-14-042208-0 $ 14.95

FRANÇOIS VILLON
1431–1480, FRENCH

Selected Poems

Translated by Peter Dale

This edition of the vibrant poems of Villon—vagabond, thief, murderer, and poet—contains both the original French text, and on facing pages, Peter Dale's translations.

240 pp.   0-14-042218-8 $ 10.95

VIRGIL
70 B.C.–19 B.C., ROMAN

The Eclogues
Translated and introduced by Guy Lee

Written between 42 and 37 B.C., ten pastoral poems believed to be the first authentic work by Virgil are presented with the original Latin on the left-hand page and the translation on the right.

144 pp.   0-14-044419-X $ 9.95

The Georgics
Translated and introduced by L. P. Wilkinson

The first descriptive poem in Western literature, *The Georgics* is one of the supreme achievements in Latin poetry.

160 pp.   0-14-044414-9 $ 7.95

WANG WEI
699–761, CHINESE

Poems
Translated and introduced by G. W. Robinson

Written during the T'ang period, considered the apogee of Chinese civilization, these poems by a devoted Buddhist are quiet reflections on the natural world and rural life.

144 pp.   0-14-044296-0 $ 9.95

WALT WHITMAN
1819–1892, AMERICAN

The Complete Poems
Edited by Francis Murphy

Of the nine editions Whitman prepared of his *Leaves of Grass*, this final "death bed" edition (1891–92) is printed in accordance with a note of instruction left by the poet to his future editors.

896 pp.   0-14-042222-6 $ 12.95

Leaves of Grass
Edited and introduced by Malcolm Cowley

This is the original and complete 1885 edition of one of the greatest masterpieces of American literature, including Whitman's own introduction to the work.

192 pp.   0-14-042199-8 $ 6.95

WILLIAM WORDSWORTH
1770–1850, ENGLISH

The Poems
Volume 1
Edited and introduced by John O. Hayden

The poems, arranged in chronological order, show the development of Wordsworth's themes and forms, illuminated by the editor's extensive notes. The selection includes *Lines Written as a School Exercise at Hawkshead*, *We Are Seven*, *Surprised by joy—impatient as the Wind*, and others.

1,072 pp.   0-14-042211-0 $ 17.95

Volume 2

In this volume are *Tintern Abbey, The Excursion, By the Sea-Side, Ode on the Installation of His Royal Highness Prince Albert*, and others.

1,104 pp.   0-14-042212-9 $ 17.95

The Prelude
A Parallel Text

Edited and introduced by J. C. Maxwell

Wordsworth's autobiographical masterwork is presented here in a version paralleling the first-edition text (1805–6) with the posthumous (1850) text.

576 pp.   0-14-042214-5 $ 12.95

Selected Poems

Edited by John O. Hayden

This new, generous selection of Wordsworth's best poems, freshly edited and chronologically arranged, reaffirms his status as one of literature's greatest poets.

624 pp.   0-14-042375-3 $ 10.95

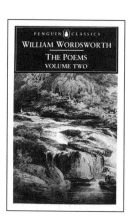

WILLIAM WORDSWORTH
1770–1850, ENGLISH
and
DOROTHY WORDSWORTH
1771–1855, ENGLISH

Home at Grasmere

Edited by Collett Clark

This perceptive arrangement of Dorothy's journal entries alongside William's poems sheds light on the poet's creative process.

302 pp.   0-14-043136-5 $ 10.95

SIR THOMAS WYATT
1503–1542, ENGLISH

The Complete Poems

Edited and introduced by R. Z. Rebholz

Written during the mid-sixteenth century, the rondeaux, sonnets, epigrams, canzoni, ballades, songs, epistolary satires, psalms, and poems of Renaissance diplomat and Tudor courtier Sir Thomas Wyatt express a high degree of intelligence and culture as surely as did his diplomatic work.

560 pp.   0-14-042227-7 $ 12.95

Ancrene Wisse
Guide for Anchoresses

Translated and introduced by
Hugh White

This classic of devotional literature, and one of the great prose works of the Middle Ages, is a fascinating look at the practices of women entering a life of solitary prayer, meditation, and ascetic religious lfe.

256 pp.　　0-14-044585-4　　$ 10.95

The Bhagavad Gita

Translated and introduced by
Juan Mascaro

One of the most important mystical poems in the Hindu scriptures, the *Bhagavad Gita* ranks among the key religious books of the world.

128 pp.　　0-14-044121-2　　$ 7.95

Buddhist Scriptures

Edited and introduced by Edward Conze

This selection of writings from the golden age of Buddhist literature (A.D. 100 to 400) focuses on texts intended for the layperson rather than for the monk and exhibits the humanity rather than the profundity of the scriptures. Passages from the *Dhammapada*, the *Buddhacarita*, the *Questions of King Milinda*, and the *Tibetan Book of the Dead* are included.

256 pp.　　0-14-044088-7　　$ 9.95

The Cistercian World
Monastic Writings of the Twelfth Century

Translated, edited, and introduced by
Pauline Matarasso

Collected in this volume are letters, sermons, biographies, satires, and stories by the influential abbot St. Bernard of Clairvaux and other monks of the Cistercian Order—the medieval order devoted to strict asceticism and a life of poverty.

336 pp.　　0-14-043356-2　　$ 12.95

The Cloud of Unknowing and Other Works

Translated and introduced by
Clifton Wolters

This devotional classic springs from the fourteenth century, an age when European mysticism was in full flower, and includes three shorter works attributed to the same writer—*The Epistle of Privy Counsel*, *Dionysius' Mystical Training (Deonise Hid Divinite)*, and *The Epistle of Prayer*—illuminating the close relationship between medieval spirituality and mysticism.

232 pp.　　0-14-044385-1　　$ 6.95

The Dhammapada

Translated and introduced by
Juan Mascaro

Compiled in the third century B.C., these aphorisms illustrate the Buddhist *dhamma*, or moral system, pointing out the narrow Path of Perfection that leads toward Nirvana.

96 pp.   0-14-044284-7 $ 6.95

Early Christian Writings
The Apostolic Fathers

Revised and introduced by
Andrew Louth
Translated by Maxwell Staniforth

These letters and small-scale theological treatises provide a rich articulation of the emerging traditions and organization of the infant Church.

208 pp.   0-14-044475-0 $ 8.95

The Epic of Gilgamesh

Translated and introduced by
N. K. Sandars

Fifteen centuries before Homer, this great Mesopotamian epic prefigures the mythology of many of the world's religions. N. K. Sandars's straightforward English version is accompanied by a comprehensive introduction tracing the literary, historical, and archaeological background of Gilgamesh.

128 pp.   0-14-044100-X $ 6.95

Hindu Myths

Translated by Wendy Doniger

This selection and translation of seventy-five seminal myths spans a wide range of Indian sources, from the serpent-slaying Indra of the *Vedas* to the medieval pantheon.

268 pp.   0-14-044306-1 $ 9.95

The Koran

Translated and introduced by
N. J. Dawood

Dawood's vivid revised translation is presented with opposing-page parallel Arabic text in the traditional calligraphic style. The volume includes a comprehensive index. Oversized format.

1,082 pp.   0-14-044542-0 $ 19.95

The Koran
Revised Edition

Translated and introduced with notes by
N. J. Dawood

This classic, authoritative translation has been newly revised to fully reflect the characteristic flavor and rhythm of the sacred work, following the original sequence of the Koranic suras.

456 pp.   0-14-044558-7 $ 6.95

Poems of Heaven and Hell from Ancient Mesopotamia

Translated and introduced by
N. K. Sandars

Five poems from the height of Babylonian civilization reflect the cyclical nature of the lives and beliefs of the Mesopotamian culture. Included are *The Babylonian Creation, The Sumerian Underworld, Inanna's Journey to Hell, Adapa: The Man,* and *A Prayer to the Gods of Night.*

192 pp.   0-14-044249-9 $ 9.95

The Psalms

Introduced by Nicholas De Lange
Translated by Peter Levi

Universal in theme and profound in their expression of religious feeling, these psalms of the Davidic dynasty transcend the theological boundaries between Judaism and Christianity with their beauty and spirituality.

272 pp.   0-14-044319-3 $ 7.95

The Rig Veda

Translated and edited by
Wendy Doniger O'Flaherty

This collection of more than 1,000 Sanskrit hymns from the timeless world of myth and ritual forms a unique insight into early Indian mythology, philosophy, and religion.

502 pp.   0-14-044402-5 $ 9.95

Speaking of Siva

Translated and introduced by
A. K. Ramanujian

This volume contains a collection of *vacanas* (free-verse lyrics) centering on the Hindu god Siva, written by four saints of the great bhakti protest movement of the tenth century A.D.: Basvanna, Devara Dāsimayya, Mahaādeviyakka, and Allama Prabhu.

208 pp.   0-14-044270-7 $ 9.95

The Upanishads

Translated by Juan Mascaro

First written in Sanskrit between 800 and 400 B.C., these spiritual treatises form the foundation of Hindu beliefs.

144 pp.   0-14-044163-8 $ 6.95

ADOMNÁN OF IONA
C. 625–704, IRISH

Life of St. Columba

*Translated and introduced by
Richard Sharpe*

This biography, written one hundred
years after the death of St. Columba
(c. 597) and drawing on both oral and
written materials, presents a richly detailed portrait of the religious life in the
sixth century.

432 pp.   0-14-044462-9 $ 12.95

ANSELM
C. 1034–1109, CHRISTIAN SAINT

The Prayers and Meditations of St. Anselm

*Foreword by R. W. Southern
Translated by Sr. Benedicta Ward*

Combining personal ardor and scrupulous theology, *The Prayers and Meditations* offers an intimate view of this
Archbishop of Canterbury, most noted
for his acceptance of rational inquiry
into the mysteries of faith.

288 pp.   0-14-044278-2 $ 10.95

FARID UD-DIN ATTAR
C. 1142–1220, PERSIAN

The Conference of Birds

*Translated and introduced by
Afkham Darbandi and Dick Davis*

This great twelfth-century mystical
poem is an allegorical rendering of the
Way of the Sufi—the most secret and
paradoxical form of Islam.

240 pp.   0-14-044434-3 $ 9.95

AUGUSTINE
354-430, CHRISTIAN SAINT

City of God

*Edited by David Knowles
Translated by Henry Bettenson*

Augustine examines the inefficacy of
the Roman gods, and of human civilization in general. Blending Platonism
with Christianity, he created the first
Christian theology of history—
planning a city based not on the Roman
pantheon but on Christian love.

1,150 pp.   0-14-044426-2 $ 14.95

Confessions

*Translated and introduced by
R. S. Pine-Coffin*

Augustine's revealing autobiography
provides an unsurpassed analysis of the
Christian experience in the face of sin.

352 pp.   0-14-044114-X $ 7.95

JOHN BUNYAN
1628–1688, ENGLISH

Grace Abounding to
the Chief of Sinners

Edited and introduced by W. R. Owens

Bunyan's spiritual autobiography relates
his religious awakening and eventual
triumph over doubt and despair as it
charts the experience of his conversion.

144 pp.   0-14-043280-9 $ 8.95

MEISTER ECKHART
c. 1260–1327, GERMAN

Selected Writings

*Translated, edited, and introduced by
Oliver Davies*

Including some works translated into
English for the first time, *Selected Writings* illuminates the German Dominican
Meister Eckhart's synthesis of traditional Christian belief and Greek metaphysics, yielding a boldly speculative
philosophy founded on "Oneness" of
the universe and on a God at once personal and transcendent.

336 pp.   0-14-043343-0 $ 11.95

EUSEBIUS
c. 260–c. 339, CHRISTIAN SAINT

The History of the Church

*Revised, edited, and introduced by Andrew Louth
Translated by G. A. Williamson*

A clear, readable translation of the ten
books of Bishop Eusebius's *Ecclesiastical
History*—the only surviving record of
the Church during its crucial first three
hundred years—this edition recounts
the martyrdoms, heresies, schisms, and
proceedings that led to Nicaea and
other great church councils.

440 pp.   0-14-044535-8 $ 11.95

WALTER HILTON
c. 1340–1396, ENGLISH

The Ladder of Perfection

Translated by Leo Sherley-Price

A superb example of medieval mystical
prose, this fourteenth-century doctrine
on the pursuit of spiritual salvation
through religious contemplation continues to inspire with its language of
pure and simple beauty.

288 pp.   0-14-044511-0 $ 6.95

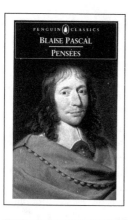

WILLIAM JAMES
1842–1910, AMERICAN

The Varieties of Religious Experience
A Study in Human Nature

Edited and introduced by Martin E. Marty

In this synthesis of religion and psychology, James discusses conversion, repentance, and other religious experiences in terms of the individual experience rather than the precepts of organized religion.

576 pp.   0-14-039034-0 $ 9.95

JULIAN OF NORWICH
1342–C. 1416, ENGLISH

Revelations of Divine Love
Translated and introduced by Clifton Wolters

This account of the sixteen visions of Mother Julian of Norwich and her meditations on her mystical experience expresses profound theology in simple language.

224 pp.   0-14-044177-8 $ 9.95

LAO TZU
6TH CENT. B.C., CHINESE

Tao Te Ching
Translated and introduced by D. C. Lau

The principal classic in the thought of Taoism is presented in this lucid English translation.

192 pp.   0-14-044131-X $ 6.95

R. K. NARAYAN
B. 1906, INDIAN

The Rāmayāna

For a description, see LITERATURE.

JOHN HENRY NEWMAN
1801–1890, ENGLISH

Apologia pro Vita Sua
Edited and introduced by Ian Ker

A spiritual autobiography of great power, *Apologia pro Vita Sua* was written in response to personal attacks and conceived as a justification of his own actions when Newman's conversion to Roman Catholicism rocked the Church of England and escalated the spread of anti-Catholicism in Victorian England.

608 pp.   0-14-043374-0 $ 12.95

BLAISE PASCAL
1623–1662, FRENCH

Pensées
Translated by A. J. Krailsheimer

Pensées is a collection of short writings that ponder the contrast between man in his fallen state and in a state of grace. It is a work of extraordinary literary power; a lucid, eloquent, and often satirical look at human illusions, self-deceptions, and follies.

368 pp.   0-14-044645-1 $ 9.95

The Provincial Letters
Translated and introduced by A. J. Krailsheimer

The sheer brilliance of Pascal's intellect in these nineteen letters—rife with blistering satire of the irresponsible frivolity of the Jesuits—has excited the admiration of generations of readers from Voltaire and Sainte-Beuve to Michel Foucault.

304 pp.   0-14-044196-4 $ 7.95

RICHARD ROLLE
c. 1300–1349, ENGLISH

The Fire of Love
Translated and introduced by Clifton Wolters

Part autobiography and part practical guide to the devout life, *The Fire of Love* is the best known of Rolle's writings, an intense document of the fourteenth-century mystic's love of God.

192 pp.   0-14-044256-1 $ 9.95

THOMAS À KEMPIS
c. 1379–1471, GERMAN

The Imitation of Christ
Translated by Leo Sherley-Price

One of the most read and influential of Christian classics, this is a seminal work of the "Devotio Moderna," the late medieval reform movement which returned to the original Apostolic zeal and simplicity of Christianity.

234 pp.   0-14-044027-5 $ 7.95

TIRUVALLUVAR
c. 2ND CENT., INDIAN

The Kural
Translated and introduced by P. S. Sundaram

Written between the second century B.C. and the eighth century A.D., *The Kural* comprises 1,330 couplets based on the first three supreme Hindu aims: virtue (*dharma*), wealth (*artha*), and love (*kama*).

168 pp.   0-14-044583-8 $ 7.95

Beowulf

For a description, see LITERATURE.

Early Irish Myths and Sagas

Translated, edited, and introduced by Jeffrey Gantz

The fourteen myths and tales collected in this volume represent the foremost written repository of Celtic oral tradition, considered the earliest voice of Western civilization.

288 pp.   0-14-044397-5 $ 9.95

Egil's Saga

Translated and introduced by Hermann Pálsson and Paul Edwards

Thought to have been written in 1230, *Egil's Saga* chronicles the histories of the ruling clans of Iceland and Norway, giving a wide-ranging view of the Viking world in the ninth and tenth centuries.

256 pp.   0-14-044321-5 $ 10.95

Eyrbyggja Saga

Translated and introduced by Hermann Pálsson and Paul Edwards

Of this mid-thirteenth-century saga, Sir Walter Scott remarked: "Of all the various records of Icelandic history and literature, there is none more interesting than *Eyrbyggja Saga*."

192 pp.   0-14-044530-7 $ 8.95

Hrafnkel's Saga

Translated by Hermann Pálsson

These seven stories, dating from the thirteenth century, combine pagan elements and Christian ethics; some are set in the pastoral society of Iceland, while others are concerned with the royal courts of Norway and Denmark.

144 pp.   0-14-044238-3 $ 9.95

Laxdaela Saga

Translated by Magnus Magnusson and Hermann Pálsson

This dynastic chronicle, composed around 1245, sweeps across 150 years of Iceland's early history.

272 pp.   0-14-044218-9 $ 9.95

The Mabinogion

Translated and introduced by Jeffrey Gantz

A combination of fact and fantasy, myth, history, and folklore, these tales from the Welsh oral tradition were first written down in the thirteenth century.

372 pp.   0-14-044322-3 $ 5.95

Njal's Saga

Translated by Magnus Magnusson and Hermann Pálsson

Based on historical events in tenth-century Iceland, this spare, simple narrative describes a fifty-year blood feud from its violent beginnings to its tragic end.

384 pp.   0-14-044103-4 $ 9.95

Orkneyinga Saga
The History of the Earls of Orkney

Translated by Hermann Pálsson and Paul Edwards

Describing the conquest of the Orkney Islands by the Kings of Norway, this is the only medieval Norse chronicle concerned with what is now part of the British Isles.

250 pp.   0-14-044383-5 $ 8.95

THE ICELANDIC & SCANDINAVIAN SAGAS

"Sagas" are anonymous prose narratives written mainly in the thirteenth and fourteenth centuries. The word implies both "history" and "story," and though they are about historical figures they are composed with inventive literary skill. They may be massive, covering the lives of several generations, as in *Njal*, *Laxdaela*, *Egil*, and *Eyrbyggja*, the latter an acknowledged influence on Scott, or short stories such as *Hrafnkel*. All these are about the families of warrior-farmers and adventurers who settled in Iceland in the tenth and eleventh centuries. Others, such as *Orkneyinga* and *King Harold's Saga*, record the history of Scandinavian ruling families.

The great Scandinavian seafarers explored south to North Africa and the Mediterranean, eastward up the rivers of Russia, and west to Greenland and North America. The latter journeys are to be found in *The Vinland Sagas*. Such travels encouraged a taste for fantasy — entertainments such as those in *Seven Viking Romances,* which display French influences — but the great sagas are a native growth, unique in medieval European literature for their naturalistic re-creation of a way of life.

Seven Viking Romances

*Translated and introduced by
Hermann Pálsson and Paul Edwards*

Incorporating local myths and legends,
as well as sources from Homer to
French romances, these medieval stories
feature famous kings, difficult gods, and
great adventures.

304 pp.   0-14-044474-2 $ 8.95

The Vinland Sagas and The Norse Discovery of America

*Translated by Magnus Magnusson and
Hermann Pálsson*

These two Icelandic sagas tell the arresting stories of the discovery of America
five centuries before the arrival of
Christopher Columbus.

126 pp.   0-14-044154-9 $ 6.95

SNORRI STURLUSON
1179–1241, ICELANDIC

King Harald's Saga

*Translated by Magnus Magnusson and
Hermann Pálsson*

The biography of one of the most remarkable and memorable of the medieval kings of Norway, this saga
culminates in the conflict between Norway and England in 1066.

192 pp.   0-14-044183-2 $ 8.95

SCIENCE

CHARLES DARWIN
1809–1882, ENGLISH

The Origin of Species

Edited by J. W. Burrow

The foundation of our current understanding about the place of humanity in
the universe, *The Origin of Species* revolutionized the history of scientific and
philosophical thought.

480 pp.   0-14-043205-1 $ 8.95

The Voyage of the Beagle
Charles Darwin's Journal of Researches

*Edited and introduced by Janet Browne
and Michael Neue*

This shortened version of Darwin's
journal of his five-year voyage on the
H.M.S. *Beagle* provides a profusion of
detail about natural history and geology
and illuminates the local people, politics, and customs.

448 pp.   0-14-043268-X $ 10.95

GILBERT WHITE
1720–1793, ENGLISH

The Natural History of Selborne
Edited by Richard Mabey

First published in 1788–89, this beautifully written evocation of the natural world continues to shape our everyday view of the relationship between human beings and nature.

320 pp. 0-14-043112-8 $ 8.95

TRAVEL

Colonial American Travel Narratives

For a description, see HISTORY AND POLITICS.

MARQUIS DE CUSTINE
1790–1857, FRENCH

Letters from Russia
Edited and introduced by Robin Buss

This striking travelogue, written in 1839 by an aristocratic Frenchman, offers a fascinating "outsider's" perspective of a vast and varied country caught in the grip of tsarist tyranny.

288 pp. 0-14-044548-X $ 9.95

DANIEL DEFOE
1660–1731, ENGLISH

A Tour Through the Whole Island of Great Britain

For a description, see LITERATURE.

GERALD OF WALES
C. 1146–C. 1223, WELSH

The Journey Through Wales, The Description of Wales

For a description, see HISTORY AND POLITICS.

JOHANN W. VON GOETHE
1749–1832, GERMAN

Italian Journey
Translated and introduced by W. H. Auden and Elizabeth Mayer

Goethe's account of his passage through Italy from 1786 to 1788 is one of the great travel chronicles of any era, as well as a candid self-portrait of a genius in the grip of spiritual crisis.

512 pp. 0-14-044233-2 $ 11.95

GRAHAM GREENE
1904–1991, ENGLISH

In Search of a Character

Two fascinating journals from Greene's visits to Africa—where he set two of his novels, *A Burnt-Out Case* and *The Heart of the Matter*—provide an absorbing glimpse of the novelist responding to the raw material of his art.

20TH-CENTURY CLASSICS

112 pp.   0-14-018578-X $ 8.95

Journey Without Maps

This chronicle of Greene's journey through Liberia in the 1930s is at once vivid reportage and a powerful document of spiritual hunger and renewal.

20TH-CENTURY CLASSICS

256 pp.   0-14-018579-8 $ 9.95

The Lawless Roads

This story of Greene's visit to Mexico emerged after he was commissioned to find out how the ordinary people had reacted to the brutal anti-clerical purges of President Calles.

20TH-CENTURY CLASSICS

224 pp.   0-14-018580-1 $ 9.95

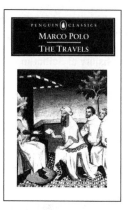

LAFCADIO HEARN
1850–1904, ENGLISH

Writings from Japan
An Anthology

Edited and introduced by Francis King

Lafcadio Hearn's bohemian sensibility, his taste for the exotic, and his enthusiastic immersion in his adopted culture sparkle in this entertaining, idiosyncratic celebration of Japan.

368 pp.   0-14-043463-1 $ 10.95

HENRY JAMES
1843–1916, AMERICAN

The American Scene

Edited and introduced by John F. Sears

The American Scene is a haunting, brilliant journal by one of America's greatest literary observers, published in 1907, after James's final journey through this country after living abroad for twenty years.

400 pp.   0-14-043416-X $ 11.95

Italian Hours

Edited and introduced with notes by
John Auchard

In these essays on travels in Italy, written from 1872 to 1909, Henry James explores art and religion, political shifts and cultural revolutions, his own ambivalent reactions to the transformations of nineteenth-century Europe and the nature of travel itself.

416 pp.   0-14-043507-7 $ 11.95

SAMUEL JOHNSON
and JAMES BOSWELL
1709–1784; 1740–1795, ENGLISH

A Journey to the Western Islands of Scotland and The Journal of a Tour to the Hebrides

Edited and introduced by Peter Levi

The remarkable friendship between Johnson and Boswell is celebrated in these complementary journals written during their tour of Scotland in 1773. Abridged.

272 pp.   0-14-043221-3 $ 10.95

SIR JOHN MANDEVILLE
14TH CENT., ENGLISH

The Travels of Sir John Mandeville

Translated and introduced by
Charles Moseley

Though it is still disputed if, and how far, Mandeville actually travelled, his travelogue was consulted for hard geographical information by da Vinci and Columbus and stands today as a unique portrait of fourteenth-century Europe.

208 pp.   0-14-044435-1 $ 9.95

MARCO POLO
1254–1324, VENETIAN

The Travels

Translated and introduced by
Ronald Latham

Marco Polo's chronicle of his travels, whether read as fact or fiction, remains a classic of travel literature, alive with adventures, geographical information, and descriptions of natural phenomena.

384 pp.   0-14-044057-7 $ 5.95

J. M. SYNGE
1871–1909, IRISH

The Aran Islands

Edited and introduced by Tim Robinson

The dramatic record of Synge's visit to the savagely beautiful Aran Islands at the turn of the century, this work is drenched in the Gaelic soul of Ireland.

20TH-CENTURY CLASSICS

208 pp.   0-14-018432-5 $ 9.95

REBECCA WEST
1892–1983, ENGLISH

Black Lamb and Grey Falcon
A Journey through Yugoslavia

For a description, see HISTORY AND POLITICS.

Aphra Behn
Love Letters between a Nobleman
and his Sister

Saul Bellow
The Adventures of Augie March
Humboldt's Gift
Henderson the Rain King
Mosby's Memoirs and Other Stories
Herzog

Andrei Bely
Petersburg

Elizabeth Browning
Aurora Leigh and Other Poems

Joseph Conrad
The Rescue

F. Scott Fitzgerald
This Side of Paradise

Gustave Flaubert
Flaubert in Egypt

Theodore Fontane
Woman Taken in Adultery

Stella Gibbons
Cold Comfort Farm

Graham Greene
The Captain and the Enemy

Lady Gregory
Selected Writings

John Hawkes
Three Novels:
The Lime Twig
Second Skin
Travesty

D. H. Lawrence
Selected Letters

Sinclair Lewis
Babbitt

Medieval English Lyrics
Tom Duncan, editor

Herman Melville
Pierre or The Ambiguities

Robert Musil
Posthumous Papers of a Living Author

Shiva Naipaul
Man of Mystery and Other Stories
A Hot Country
Fireflies

Luigi Pirandello
Six Characters in Search of an Author

John Steinbeck
Sweet Thursday
Winter of Our Discontent

Rabindranath Tagore
The Home and the World

Leo Tolstoy
What Is Art?

Anthony Trollope
He Knew He Was Right
The Prime Minister
The Duke's Children
Rachel Ray

Edith Wharton
The Age of Innocence

Antonia White
Frost in May

Virginia Woolf
Night and Day

William Butler Yeats
The Short Fiction of Yeats

COMING TO PENGUIN CLASSICS ON AUDIO FOR 1996

Louisa May Alcott
Little Women

Jane Austen
Persuasion
Sense and Sensibility
Mansfield Park

Anne Brontë
The Tenant of Wildfell Hall

Frances Burnett
Little Princess

Lewis Carroll
Alice in Wonderland

Daniel Defoe
Moll Flanders

Charles Dickens
Nicholas Nickleby

Thomas Hardy
The Mayor of Casterbridge
Tess of the D'Urbervilles

Henry James
Portrait of a Lady

Jack London
White Fang

Herman Melville
Moby-Dick

A. A. Milne
House at Pooh Corner

Beatrix Potter
Complete Tales

Anna Sewell
Black Beauty

Mark Twain
Huckleberry Finn

Edith Wharton
The Age of Innocence

Arthur Miller
The Crucible
CD-ROM

Bringing the resources of the greatest libraries to the study of Arthur Miller's powerful drama, *The Crucible CD-ROM* presents a rich multimedia experience, including the full text of the play with annotations; archival materials on the Salem trials and the 1950s McCarthy hearings that inspired Miller to write the play; video of a theatrical performance and of renowned performers discussing their experience of the play; and an extensive video interview with Arthur Miller.

MAC, Book and CD-ROM
0-14-0242777-5 $64.95

MPC, CD-ROM only
1-57395-003-3 $49.95

LITERATURE

John Steinbeck
Of Mice and Men
CD-ROM

This electronic study guide and companion to Steinbeck's classic novel includes the entire text of the book linked to such resources as video interviews with the author's biographer, Jackson Benson, and his widow, Elaine Steinbeck; extensive critical commentary by leading Steinbeck scholars, including Susan Shillinglaw; photographs, maps, and period music performed by Woody Guthrie; scenes from the 1992 film based on the book; and fascinating archival material.

MPC
1-57395-001-7 $49.95

MAC
1-57395-000-9 $49.95

LITERATURE

INDEX

A

D

E

F

G

L

M

U

V

W